FREDERICK LOEWE
ALAN JAY LERNER

PAINT YOUR WAGON

CHAPPELL
& CO • INC •
609 FIFTH AVE.
NEW YORK 17,
N. Y.
CHAPPELL
& CO • LTD • LONDON
MADE IN U. S. A.

CHERYL CRAWFORD

presents

JAMES BARTON

in

PAINT YOUR WAGON

A Musical Play

Music by

FREDERICK LOEWE

Book and Lyrics by

ALAN JAY LERNER

Dances and Musical Ensembles by AGNES de MILLE

Scenery Designed by
OLIVER SMITH

Costumes Designed by
MOTLEY

Orchestra and chorus conducted by FRANZ ALLERS

Lighting by
PEGGY CLARK

Orchestrations by
TED ROYAL

Music for dances arranged by TRUDE RITTMAN

Production Associate, BEA LAWRENCE

Entire Production Directed by DANIEL MANN

VOCAL SCORE

EDITED BY FRANZ ALLERS

First performance at the Sam S. Shubert Theatre, New York
November 12, 1951

PAINT YOUR WAGON

Cast of Characters

WALT	Bert Matthews
JENNIFER RUMSON	Olga San Juan
SALEM TRUMBULL	Ralph Bunker
JASPER	Ted Thurston
BEN RUMSON	James Barton
STEVE BULLNACK	Rufus Smith
PETE BILLINGS	James Mitchell
CHERRY	Kay Medford
JAKE WHIPPANY	Robert Penn
MIKE MOONEY	John Randolph
LEE ZEN	Chun-Tao Cheng
DOCTOR NEWCOMB	David Thomas
EDGAR CROCKER	Richard Aherne
SANDY TWIST	Jared Reed
REUBEN SLOANE	Gordon Dilworth
JULIO VALVERAS	Tony Bavaar
JACOB WOODLING	Josh Wheeler
ELIZABETH WOODLING	Marijane Maricle
SARAH WOODLING	Jan Sherwood
DUTCHIE	Bert Matthews
CARMELLITA	Lorraine Havercroft
YVONNE SOREL	Gemze de Lappe
SUZANNE DUVAL	Mary Burr
RAYMOND JANNEY	Gordon Dilworth
ROCKY	James Tarbutton
ED	Edgar Thompson
JACK	Delbert Anderson
BILL	Norman Weise
SAM	Feodore Tedick
JOHANSEN	John Anderson

(Miners, Fandangos)

Instruments of the Orchestra in the New York Production*

WOODWINDS (*W'winds.*):

1st Player: Flute (*Fl.*); Piccolo (*Picc.*); Clarinet (*Clar.*); Alto Sax.

2nd Player: Flute; Piccolo; Clarinet; Alto Sax.

3rd Player: Oboe; Clarinet; Tenor Sax.

4th Player: Clarinet; Bass Clarinet; Tenor Sax.

5th Player: Bassoon (*Bssn.*); Flute; Piccolo; Clarinet; Bass Clarinet; Baritone Sax.

BRASS (*Br.*):

3 French Horns (*Hn.*)

3 Trumpets (*Tpt.*)

2 Trombones (*Trmb.*)

1 Percussion (*Timp.; Dr.*)

1 Piano, doubling Celesta

1 Banjo, doubling Guitar (*Guit.*)

STRINGS (*Str.*):

8 Violins (*Vln.*); *A* and *B*

2 Violas (*Vla.*); one doubling Mandolin (*Mand.*)

2 'Celli

2 Basses (*Bs.*), one doubling Tuba

The rehearsal numbers circled in the score correspond to those in the orchestra parts, but do not represent an actual numbering of bars because of cuts and changes in the production during the tryout period.

*The wind parts have been condensed for 1 Flute, 1 Oboe, 2 Clarinets doubling Saxophones, and 1 Bassoon; and have been cross-cued for any smaller number of players. In small orchestras, 2 Trumpets and 1 Trombone are advisable.

MUSICAL PROGRAM

ACT I

ACT II

OVERTURE

No. 1

FREDERICK LOEWE

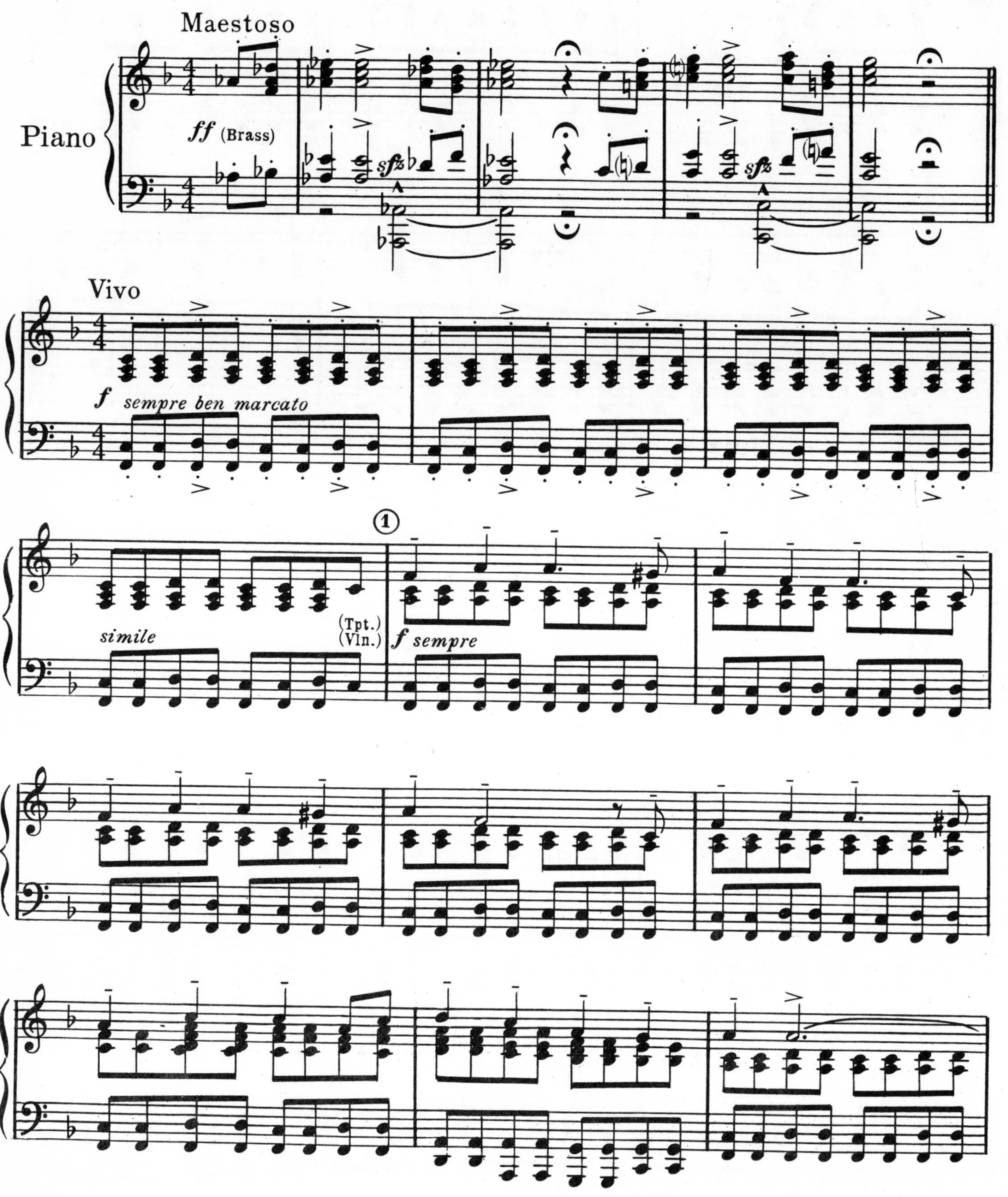

1876

mf
espr.
simile
f

ff
crescendo
fff
② Moderato
f
(Tutti)
mf
(Hrn.)
p
③
L.H.
L.H.
(Str.)
p espr.

L.H.
f
poco rit.
sempre f a tempo
L.H.
mf (Tpt.)

p (Vlns.)
f (Tutti)
poco rit.
④ Tempo di marcia
simile
f subito
crescendo
⑤
ff

f (Trmb.)
(Tutti)
L.H.
ff
⑥
poco rit.

⑦ Moderato
fp
mf
⑨
f
⑰

ff
dimin.
pp
cresc. molto
⑧ Vivace
(Banjo)
ff
(Trmb.)

(Tutti)
(♩ = 𝅗𝅥)
sempre ff
(Tuba)
sffz
attacca

Introduction to Scene I

No. 2

I'm On My Way

Lyrics by
ALAN JAY LERNER

Music by
FREDERICK LOEWE

No. 3

Cue: JENNIFER: Look, pa! Gold! Gold!

BEN: So anyhow, here's Jim, Lord. I hope you'll make him happy up there.... for-ever-and-ever-I-stake-this-claim-Amen!

(The music begins)

42
I gotta strike it and get home to my wife. PETE: Where
north you goin'? STEVE: I'll find out when I get there.
(Banjo) p marcato
50
STEVE:
Where'm I go - in'? I don't know. Where am I head - in'? I ain't cer - tain.
(Str.) mf con spirito
All I know is I am on my way.
(W.Winds)

58
When will I be there? I don't know. When will I get there? I ain't cer - tain.
All I know is I am on my way!
Got a
66
dream, boy?
Got a song?
Paint your
wa - gon
And come a - long!

(74)

Where am I go - in'? I don't know. When will I be there? I ain't cer-tain.

What will I get? I ain't e - quipped to say, ___ But

(82)

who gives a damn, we're on our way! ___ (Clar.)

(Brass)

pp

(86)

CHERRY: You have to go, Jake? You have to leave me? JAKE: I got to,

94
Cherry. I ain't hittin' nothin' but slate rock a - round here. CHERRY:
(Str.)
p cantando
(Horn)
Jakie, I love you. Why is there so much money you do not have?
(Banjo)
102
JAKE: This time I'll make it, honey. I got a hunch
p scherzando
my luck is gonna change. And when it does, you know what
(Oboe)
110
I'm gonna do? I'm goin' to open the gol darndest music hall that Californy ever
(Clar.)

114

saw. Velvet and satin wherever you look. And some of that real Frenchy wine.

118

CHERRY: And you send for me and I close my house and bring my girls up to you. Make all the

(Strings)

122

miners very happy. JAKE: Yeah, honey. That's what you do. CHERRY: Don't make me wait too long. I want

to stay true to you. JAKE: Don't worry, honey.... Come on, little banjo! Lead me to the rainbow!

130

JAKE:

Where'm I go - in'? I don't know. Where am I head - in'? I ain't cer - tain.

mf con spirito

All I know is I am on my way.
138
When will I be there? I don't know. When will I get there? I ain't cer-tain.
SIX MINERS:
All I know is I am on my way! Got a
f (Brass)
146
dream, boy? Got a song? Paint your

wa - gon And come a - long!
marc.

154
MIKE: It's north I want to go, Doctor. North. Beyond the redwood country. I met an old man in
pp subito
(Str.)

Sacramento who swears, by the saints, there's a lake o' gold up there. You hear me? A lake with a

(Oboe)

162
bottom of solid gold! DOCTOR: I'm goin' where the gold is in the ground. MIKE: But look, Doctor.
(Flute)

170
Look at this map! It shows you just how to get there.
mp (Banjo)
DOCTOR: I'm going to Rumson Creek. So long.
MIKE: I'm comin'. Wait a minute!
poco cresc.
178
MIKE:
Where'm I go - in'? I don't know. Where am I head-in'? I ain't cer-tain.
mf animato

All I know is I am on my way.
(Vlns.)
186
When will I be there? I don't know. When will I get there? I ain't cer-tain.
TEN MINERS:
All I know is I am on my way! Got a
f (add Horn, Trmb)
194
dream, boy? Got a song? Paint your

* Cantonese dialect, transcribed into approximate English phonetics.

212
CROCKER: I say, guv'nor, isn't this Sawmill
chin.
money.
dimin. (Strings)
pp
Camp? SANDY: Yeh, what's left of it. REUBEN: The gold run out, pardner. SANDY:
220
In a week you won't find enough dust around here to fill a bug's nose.
CROCKER: Now, ain't that the bloomin' luck. Where are you bound now, gentlemen?
228
REUBEN: To Rumson Creek. You want to come with us? CROCKER: I'd like to very much, guv'nor.
(Banjo)

SANDY: What's your statistics, pardner? CROCKER: Edgar Crocker, from London,
England. SANDY: Well, come along then, Edgar Crocker, from London,
(W. Winds)
cresc.
England!
poco a poco
f cresc. molto
(Tutti)
EVERYBODY:
Where'm I go - in'? I don't know. Where am I head - in'? I ain't cer - tain.
ff

All I know is I am on my way!
TENOR
244
When will I be there? I don't know. When will I get there? I ain't cer - tain,
BARITONE
BASS
When will I be there? I don't know. When will I get there? I ain't cer - tain,
All I know is I am on my way! Got a
All I know is I am on my way! Got a
fff pesante
(Trmb. Tuba)

252

dream, boy? Got a song? Paint your

dream, boy? Got a song? Paint your

wa - gon And come a - long!

wa - gon And come a - long!

260

Where am I go - in'? I don't know. When will I be there? I ain't cer - tain.

Where am I go - in'? I don't know. When will I be there? I ain't cer - tain.

ff

What will I get? I ain't e-quipped to say, But
What will I get? I ain't e-quipped to say, But
268
272
div.
who gives a damn, We're on our way!
who gives a damn, We're on our way!
ff sempre
f
sffz Attacca

Rumson Town

No. 4

hun-dred peo-ple came to Rum-son Creek! Came from
just four hun-dred men at Rum-son Creek! There was
Ten-nes-see and Maine,_ From Chi-na, France and Spain;_Came the
booze e nough to swim in, But not a sign of wo-men; There were
gold dust for to see to Rum-son Creek! 2. There were
just four hun-dred men at Rum-son
1.
2.
Creek!
PETE: Where'd you get the paper, Salem? (The dialogue continues.)
mf
(Banjo)
diminuendo
p
pp

What's Goin' On Here?

No. 5

Cue: SALEM: How did the Lord mayor do today?
JENNIFER: Fine. Salem, what's the matter with everyone around here? They're gettin' stranger and stranger every day.
(The music begins)

1876

go - in' on? What's in the
26
air? The way this town's be - hav - in' is e - nough to make a
per - son tear her hair.
8va
(W. Winds)
leggiero
f p (Clar.)
poco rit. mf
34
Moderato
I sit down to tie my shoe and ev - 'ry sin - gle time I do, I'm
p (Str.)

cir - cled by a hun - dred men or more.
f marc.
(Trmb.)
42
What's go - in' on here? What's go - in' on? Ain't
p
no one ev - er seen a shoe be - fore?
(W.Winds)
f
mf
50
Lift - in' me a - cross the mud, A min - er dropped me with a thud And
p (Str.)

said he'd nev - er pick me up a - gain.
f marc.
(Trmb.)
58
What's go - in' on here? What's go - in' on? I
p
(Brass)
on - ly weigh a hun-dred nine or ten. I nev - er
(W. Winds)
f
p (Str.)
66
seen a camp so cra - zy. They must - 've

all had too much sun.—— When the days are hot as steam And ev-'ry one goes in the stream, When I jump in, they all jump out and run.—— Oh, What's go-in' on here? What's go-in' on here? What —— did

(74) (82)

(W. Winds) (Brass) mf p (Str.) p (Horns, Cl.) (Brass)

90

I done?

(W. Winds) *cre - scen - do*

f

ff (Tutti)

94

Commodo (♩ = 𝅗𝅥)

No one will walk with me. Ev-'ry-one leaves me high and dry.

p (Str.)

No one will talk with me. Tell me why, why, why?

(Bs. Cl.)

mf

MIKE: Y'see, Jen, you may have noticed that with the exception of yourself, practically everybody here is o' the opposite gender. It means...well, it means that...when little boys start findin' out

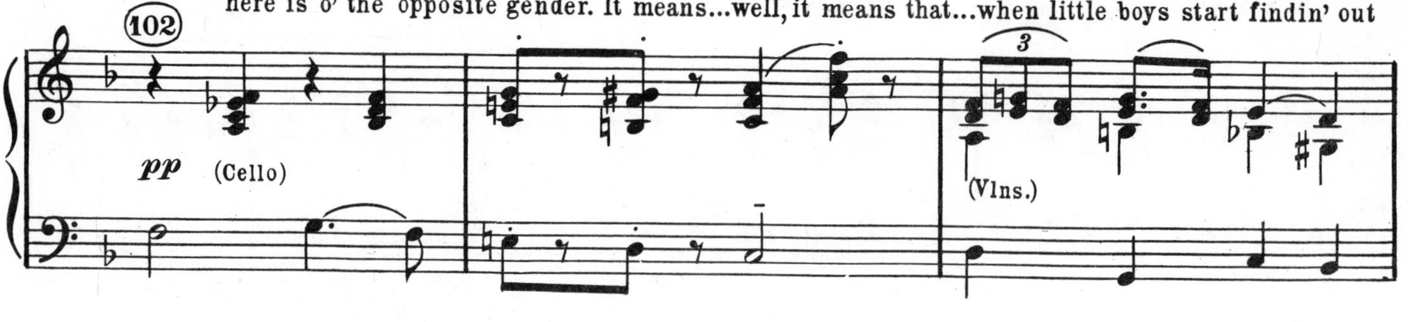

102

pp (Cello)

(Vlns.)

that little girls ain't little boys, they start lookin' for little girls... and... well...
Damn it! You shouldn't be passin' him in the woods. Do you understand?
JENNIFER
No! What's goin'on here?
Allegro
110
JENNIFER:
Once I asked a min-er if he'd rub my neck 'cause
f (Tutti)
mf
p
(Str.)
it was stiff, And feel-in' like the han-dle of a mop.
f marc.
(Trmb.)
What's go-in' on here? What's go-in' on? I
p (Str.)

could - n't get the cra - zy fool to stop. Of all the
(W. Winds)
f
p (Str.)
142
camps that I have been to, I nev - er had so
lit - tle fun. Yes - ter - day I
150
(W. Winds)
mf
p (Str.)
passed a man who asked me how to clean a pan, When I bent ov - er,

158
Lord - y, did he run!
Oh, What's go - in'
on here? What's go - in' on here? What
did I done?
p (Horns, Cl.)
(Brass)
crescendo
poco - a - poco
(Tutti) crescendo
f
ff
sfz
Dialogue

No. 6

I Talk To The Trees

Cue: JULIO: Well, I, senorita Jennifer, I, Julio......I tell you. One day I write you and ask you to come visit me. And you'll write me that you will.

(The music begins.)

JULIO: And I'll take you all around my rancho, and tell you about my trip to Spain. And

then.... Don't smile. All this is going to happen. And I have never been so sure in my whole life as I am right this

minute. So what do you think of that?

JENN: Why right this minute? JULIO: Because you listen.

stars,
But they nev-er hear me.
(W. Winds)
20
The breeze has-n't time
To stop and hear what I say;
I talk to them all in vain.
28
But sud-den-ly my words
Reach some-one
mf
(Horn)

ten.
el - se's ear; Touch some-one el - se's heart - strings
ten.
36
too. I tell you my dreams And while you're
p sempre
list - 'ning to me, I sud-den-ly see them come
44
true. I can see us on an A - pril night
(Vln.)
(W. Winds)

Sip-ping bran-dy un-der-neath the stars; Read-ing po-ems in the
can - dle-light To the strum-ming of gui - tars.
(Vlns.)
poco rit.
a tempo
52
I will tell you all the books I've read; And the way I met the
(W.Winds)
King of France. Then I'll send the ser-vants off to bed

(He bows and
And I'll ask you for a dance.
cantabile
(Horn, Bs.Cl.)
invites her to dance. They do. She's hopeless, but he carries it off as if she were the greatest in the world.)
68
(Vlns.)
(Vlns.)
(Tromb.)
76
(Cls.)
(Trpt.)

84
(Horn)
(Vln.)
(Tromb.)
dimin.
(W.Winds)
JULIO:
But sud-den-ly my words ——— Reach some-one
p
Str.

JULIO: Buenos noches, señorita. You see how I walk? That's Castillian. *(He walks off. The music begins again.)*

No.6-B

*Tempo rubato

JENNIFER: Salem!

pp (Vln. Solo)

Vla.

SALEM: You still here? JENNIFER: I forgot something. I need two cakes o' washin' soap.

(Fl.)

p

JENNIFER:

18

I talk to the trees, But they don't lis - ten to me. I talk to the stars, But they nev - er hear me.

(Vlns.)

p sempre

espr.

(Cl.)

1876 *NOTE: In the New York production, this section was also sung in the keys of E and F.*

(26)

The breeze has-n't time To stop and hear what I say.

I talk to them all in vain.

(Fls.)

(34)

But sud-den-ly my words Reach some-one el - se's ear; Touch some-one

(W.Winds)

CROCKER: *(Interrupting her)*: Jennifer,... *(The dialogue continues)*

el - se's heart - strings too. I tell you my...

(Cl.)

No. 7

Lonely Men

Cue: MIKE: I know there's a lake of gold in them hills or where would the idea've come from? And one o' these days I'm gonna set out and find it. And I'll scoop out a fortune and go back and get my girl.

(The music begins.)

33

(Pete's and the miners' restless pacing gradually crystallizes into a dance of loneliness.)

(Ob.)

mf

(Bssn.
Bs.Cl.)

(Alto Sax.)

45

mf

(Fl.
Strings)

55

Cl.

f

f (add Horn)

8va bassa

(Str.)

(Tpt.)

(Trmb.)

63
(Banjo, Ten. Sax.)
f staccato
67
(Vlns.)
f legato
(Hn.)
(Alto Sax.)
75
83

(Hn.)
(Str., W.Winds)
91
f
mf
(Tpt.)
f
99
(Trmb.)
f (Tutti)

107

115

mp (Hn.)

119 (Str., W.Winds)

f

(Trmb.)

(Tutti)

127

8va

ff

8va
135
(b)
(b)
(b)
fff
8va bassa
(b)
(b)
(b)
p
(Timp.)
143
(Hn.)
mp staccato
(Ten. Sax.)
diminuendo
151
STEVE: It was my
(Cl.)
p

wife's idea, me comin' out here. I never would've thought of it, but she says, "Bullnack, what do you
(Ob.)
rall.
159
want to do, work in a factory all your life?" I says, "No." She says, "Then put your fat carcass on
Più calmo
p sempre
the wagon and go out there and dig." That's how she is. Always thinkin' of me. But sometimes
(Cl.)
(Hn.)
mp
169
I wonder if she was right. She knows I don't feel good when I'm away from her. Do you think she was
(Cl.)
pp
177
Lento
right, Mike?
(Jake begins to pluck away on his banjo)
STEVE: That's right, Jake. Play something. Let's hear somethin' besides the wind blowin' through them damn hills.
8va
(Banjo)
pp
(Vln.)
Attacca

No. 8

They Call The Wind Maria

sends the clouds a - fly - in'. Ma-ri - a makes the
(Cello)
poco rall.
moun - tains sound Like folks were up there dy - in'.
(Cls.)
mf
a tempo
(Bs.Cl.)
20
Ma - ri - a! Ma-
(Str.)
(Trmb.)
ri - a! They call the
(W. Winds)

wind Ma - ri - a!
Be-
(Brass muted)
f
Più vivo
fore I knew Ma - ri - a's name And heard her wail and
(Str., W. Winds)
(simile)
p
(simile)
whin - in', I had a girl and she had me, And the
sun was al - ways shin - in'.
But

11-A

then one day I left my girl, I left her far be-

hind me; And now I'm lost, so gol - durn lost, Not

(Cello)

poco rall.

e - ven God can find me. ___

MINERS:

Ma-

(Cls.)

mf a tempo

(Bs. Cl.)

20-A

ri - a! ___ Ma - ri - a! ___

(Str.)

f

(Trmb.)

STEVE:
They call the wind Ma -
(W.Winds)
p
28
ri - a!
MINERS:
Out
(Tutti)
ff
f
here they got a name for rain, For wind and fi - re
(Ten. Sax.)
on - ly. But when you're lost and all a - lone, There

STEVE:
ain't no word but lone - ly. And
39
I'm a lost and lone - ly man With - out a star to
(Bssn.)
p
guide me. Ma - ri - a, blow my love to me; I need my girl be -
(Vlns.)
mf
(Hns.)
(Trmb.)
Più mosso
MINERS:
side me. Ma -
f (Tutti)
f

48
ri - a!
Ma -
(Trmb.)
Ten. Sax.
ri - a!
STEVE:
They
call
the
wind
Ma -
mf
ri - a!
MINERS:
56
Ma - ri - a!
(Trpts.)
f
Tutti

Ma - ri - a!

cresc.

molto rit.

Lento

STEVE:

Tempo I° (perdendosi)

Blow my love to me.

(Hns.)

(Alto Sax.)

ff

mf

p

64

(Curtain)

(Hns.)

ppp

Attacca

No. 9

Introduction to Scene III

No. 10 Introduction to Scene IV

Cue: JENNIFER: Pa, what are you doin'?
MIKE: Shut up!

No. 11

I Still See Elisa

(pronounced Eleeza)

Cue: JENNIFER: If she was such a lady, Pa, how come she married you?
BEN: By God, I don't know.
(The music begins)

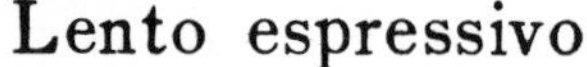

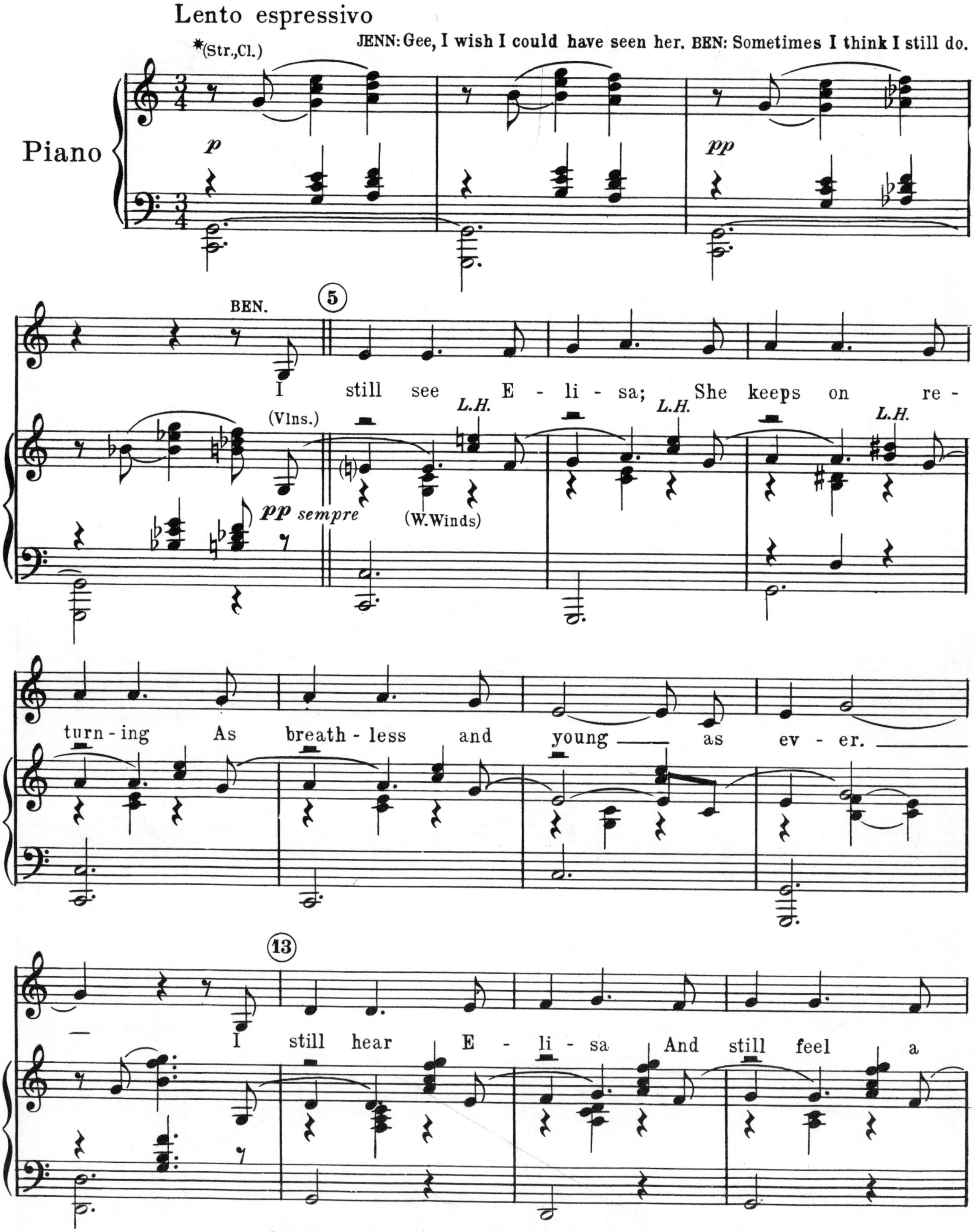
Lento espressivo
JENN: Gee, I wish I could have seen her. BEN: Sometimes I think I still do.
*(Str.,Cl.)
Piano
p
pp
BEN.
5
I still see E - li - sa; She keeps on re - turn - ing As breath - less and young as ev - er.
(Vlns.)
L.H.
pp sempre
(W.Winds)
13
I still hear E - li - sa And still feel a

NOTE: In the New York production, this number also was sung in the keys of A and Ab.

yearn - ing To hold her a - gainst me a - gain. Her
(Vlns.)
21
heart was made of hol - i - days; Her smile was made of dawn. Her
(Cls.)
L.H.
laugh - ter was an A - pril song That ech - oes on and on. Since
L.H.
(Bs. Cl.)
29
I saw E - li - sa, The shad - ows are fall - ing And
(Vlns.)

winter is calling above. But I
(Cl.)
(W.Winds)
37
still see Elisa (Strs.) When
mf espress.
(Vlns.)
pp
43
ever I dream of love.
(Cls.)
f (Strs.)
45 Cantabile
(He rises and walks away from the table, lost in the past.)
(W.Winds)
L.H.
L.H.
(Hn.)

(55) BEN:

L.H.

I still hear E - li - sa And

(Str.)

pp

(Cls.)

still feel a yearn - ing To hold her a - gainst me a -

(63)

gain.

Her heart was made of hol - i - days; Her

(Str.)

(Cl.) L.H.

smile was made of dawn. Her laugh-ter was an A - pril song That

71
ech-oes on and on. Since I saw E - li - sa, The
(Vln. Solo)
(Cls.)
shad-ows are fall - ing And win - ter is call - ing a - bove.
79
But I still see E - li - sa
(Strs.)
When-
(W.Winds, Str.)
mf espress.
pp
85
ev - er I dream of love.
Dialogue
(Cls.)
(Tutti)
mf

No. 12

How Can I Wait?

Cue: JENNIFER: What are you gonna do about me?
BEN: Clean up the cabin and go to bed.

NOTE: In the New York production, this number was also sung in the key of C.

17
wish his hands was in these sleeves, His face was in this towel. I
(add Cls.)
wish him-self was in this bag, And all of him was here. I
(Cl.)
25
wish I knew why ev-'ry night I ache and miss him so. (Spoken:) 'Specially when I'm gonna see him again tomorrow by the ravine... (sings)
Where we al - ways go. How can I
ten. ten.
(add Hn.)
mf

33
Moderato
wait, can I wait, 'til to-mor-row comes? — How can I
Vlns., Guitar, W. Winds
live 'til to-mor-row comes? — How can I make ev-'ry
41
min-ute fly — 'Til that shin-in' mo-ment when I'll be
see-in' him a-gain? I'm gon-na die, gon-na die, Or be
49
poco rit.
p a tempo
(add Hn., Guitar)

old and gray!
Why is to - mor - row so far a - way?
57
How can I talk, can I breathe, can I e-at?
p
What can I do with my hands and my fe-et?
65
How can I
p
wait, can I wait, ’til to - mor - row comes?
(Vln)
(Brass)

(71)

Star - light, go a - way, fade a - way, blow a - way!

(Str.)

pp

Sun - rise, come a - gain, make a new sun - ny day! Oh,

(♭)

riten.

(79)

what can I do can I think a - bout? How can my

(Str., Guitar, W. Winds)

mf a tempo

heart keep from jump-in' out?

(87)

How can I sleep? Could-n't

W.Winds obbl.

p

sleep if I tri-ed! Where can I run 'til I run to his
si-de? How can I wait 'til to-mor-row comes?
95
>p
(add Brass)
cresc.
poco
a
poco
mf
ff (Tutti)
105
(She dances, with Julio's shirt as her partner.)
Broadly
ff sempre
113

(Trmb.)
121
Tempo di Tango
(Guitar, Str.)
meno f
capriccioso
W. Winds
mf
129
Broadly
p (Str., W. Winds)
mf (add Hn.)
137
(add Trpts.)
f
(Str.)
(Brass)

143
JENNIFER:
Star - light, go a - way, fade a - way, blow a - way!
(Str.)
pp
Sun - rise, come a - gain, make a new sun - ny day! Oh,
(♭)
riten.
151
what can I do, can I think a - bout?
(Str., Guitar, W. Winds)
mf a tempo
How can my heart keep from jump - in' out?

BEN: *(returning to the cabin)* You know where you're goin', don't you? You're goin' East! *(Attacca)*

No. 13

I'm On My Way-Reprise

ELIZABETH:
JACOB:
SARAH:
Where'm I go - in'? I don't know. Where am I head - in'?
p (Str.)
JACOB:
I'm not cer - tain. All I know is I am on my
9-A
SARAH:
JACOB:
way. When will we be there? I dont know.
(W.Winds)
ELIZABETH:
JACOB:
SARAH and ELIZABETH:
When will we get there? I'm not cer - tain. All he knows is

JACOB:
we are on our way. Could - n't
p sempre
(Trmb.)
17-A
reck - on Where we are;
There's a cloud un - der ev - 'ry
(Trpt.)
ELIZABETH
JACOB: I told you I don't know.
(Dialogue continues)
star.
Where are we go - in'?

No. 14

Trio

Cue: JACOB: Quiet! How can I thank God for all my blessings with you two barking at each other? Both of you join me.

SARAH: Of course, Jacob. *(The music begins)*

mor - row come with - out sor - row. Be it so, we
mor - row come with - out sor - row. Be it so, we
(Hn.)
ev - er hope and pray, hope and pray.
ev - er hope and pray, hope and pray.
(Bs. Cl.)
19
SARAH:
mf
Poor dear E - liz - a - beth, her life is far from fine. But what care I? She is no
ELIZ., JACOB:
pp
Night is steal - ing o - ver and we kneel down to
pp (Strs.)

rel-a-tive of mine.
She should have thought be-fore she wore her wed-ding gown, But, no, she
pray,
For a dawn of splen - dor and a
(Hn.)
went a - head, made her bed,
Now she can't lie down.
27
The dear is al-ways work-ing
glo - ri - ous day.
May our to -
(Hn.)
Al-ways work-ing,
And that is just how
It's gon-na stay.
mor - row come with - out sor - row.

Least that's what I'll ever hope and pray, hope and pray.
(divisi)
ELIZ:
JACOB:
Be it so, we ever hope and pray, hope and pray.
(Trpts.)
f (Tutti)
(Bs. Cl.)
19-A
ELIZABETH:
mf
I have some love-ly dreams I'm long-ing to come true; We're on a lake of ice and
SARAH, JACOB
pp
Night is steal - ing o - ver and we kneel down to
pp Strs.

Sa-rah's fall-ing through. Or else we're on a hill-top look-ing at a view; a hap-py
pray, For a dawn of splen - dor and a
(Hn.)
27-A
three are we; sud-den - ly, Whoops! They're on - ly two. And would-n't it be charm-ing,
glo - ri - ous day. May our to -
(Hn.)
When we're farm-ing, If she were cut down with all the hay?
mor - row come with - out sor - row.

For that har - vest I'll ev - er hope and pray, hope and

(div.) SARAH:

JACOB:

Be it so, we ev - er hope and pray, hope and

pray. A - men.

pray. A men.

(Strs.)

(add Cls.)

mf

allarg.

42 Maestoso

(Jacob and Sarah go into the tent. Elizabeth looks after them longingly.)

f (Tutti)

46

(Curtain, Attacca)

ff rit.

Rumson Town Reprise

No. 15

Sev - en hun - dred said a prayer on Sun - day morn - in',
Oh, they held the court o' law on Sun - day morn - in',
And the one who said it quick - er was first to reach the
If they found you guilt - y Sun - day, you did - n't dig on
liq - uor, What a nois - y day it was at Rum - son
Mon - day; You were bus - y be - in' hung at Rum - son
1.
Camp.
2. Oh they
2.
Camp.
Dialogue
mf (Banjo)
sfz

No. 16

In Between

Cue: ELIZ: I don't know. I don't know anything about you.
BEN: I'm just like everybody and just like nobody. You could do worse. You could do better.
(The music begins.)

**NOTE: In the New York production, this number was also sung in the keys of G and F.*

9

tween. Now, I'm poor - er than a man who's got a
tween. Now, I've gath - er'd up a ti - dy bit o'

(Str.)

mil - lion; And I'm rich - er than a bum with-out a
learn - in'; But a col - lege would-n't pick me for the

bean. I've less than a lot have and more than some.
dean. I'm bright as the sun on a cloud - y day.

I'm in be - tween. I can
I'm in be - tween. Now, I

(Fls.) L.H. (Cl.) 8va (W.Winds) *pp sempre*

17
soak up more rye whis - key Than can
ain't ex - act - ly yel - low Or the
half the men you'll find. But there's
brav - est man you'll see. I would
(Vln. Solo)
still an - oth - er half who Can
fight a doz - en In - dians If
drink me dumb and blind. As a
fif - ty were with me. There's a
(Fls.)
(Vlns.)

25
lov - er I'd be way a - head o' man - y; But there's
thou - sand ways o' say - in' what I'm say - in'; But I'll
man - y who are way a - head o' me. And so it will go with the
tell you plain and sim - ple what I mean, I hope when you go to your
man you get: An ord - 'nar - y in be - tween he'll be. So why not
room to-night And turn down the blan-kets, I'll be seen — In be -
(Fl.)
rit.
a tempo
(Brass)
(W.Winds)
(Brass)
(W.Winds)
1.
me? 2.Now, I
2.
tween.
(W.Winds)
ff
Segue

(He dances joyously)
ff
(Tutti)
(He takes the gold from the bar and goes out)
(Brass)
(W.Winds)
(Brass)
(W.Winds)
ff (Tutti)
sfz
Dialogue

No. 17

Whoop-ti-ay!

Cue: SALEM: *(from outside)* Sold! *(The miners return with Ben, who smiles broadly and says:)*

EVERYBODY:
BEN:
cook-in'! Whoop - ti - ay! Get the corn bread cook-in'!
EVERYBODY:
BEN:
25
Whoop - ti - ay! Got a blue - eyed dai - sy to drive me cra -
- zy, It's my wed-din' day. Oh, yip-pee -
(Trpts.)
(Tutti)
33
ay! (Oh, yip - pee - ay!) Oh, yip-pee - ay! (Oh, yip - pee - ay!) I'm feel-in'
(Trmb.)
(Trmb.)

high - er than a lark can sing! Oh, what a

(41)

day! (Oh, what a day!) Oh what a day! (Oh, what a day!) I'm feel - in'

(Trmb.) (Trmb.)

hap - py as a ba - by's swing! Get the

(W.Winds) (W.Winds)(Str. obbl.)

f

(49)

bow and fid - dle! Whoop - ti - ay! Get the

Brass

ff f

57
bow and fid-dle! Whoop-ti-ay! Got a trim young
(Brass)
ff
f
fil-ly to talk me sil-ly, It's my wed-din'
63
ELIZABETH:
day! To-day is my wed-din' day.
(Fl.)
mf
BEN:
Get the
ff (Tutti)
mf (Str.)

73
EVERYBODY:
BEN:
chow - der boil - in'! Whoop - ti - ay! Get the chow - der
Brass
ff
mf
EVERYBODY:
BEN:
81
boil - in'! Whoop - ti - ay! Got a sweet per - fum-er to
(Brass)
ff
mf
ELIZABETH:
try my hu - mor; It's my wed-din' day!
Brass
p
ff
BEN:
93
EVERYBODY:
BEN:
Get the whis - key flow-in'! Whoop - ti - ay! Get the
mf (Str.)
Brass
ff
mf

101
EVERYBODY:
BEN:
whis - key flow - in'! Whoop - ti - ay! Got a sprig of
(Brass)
ff
mf
ELIZABETH:
clo - ver to make me o - ver; It's my wed-din'
p
109
EVERYBODY:
day. Oh, yip - pee - ay! (Oh, yip - pee - ay!) Oh yip - pee -
(Brass)
ff
f (Str., Brass)
ff
(W.Winds)
f
ay! (Oh, yip - pee - ay!) I'm feel - in' might - y as a red - wood
ff
f

117
tree! Oh, what a day! (Oh, what a day!) Oh, what a
day! (Oh, what a day!) I'm feel - in' flight - y as a bum - ble
bee!
125
(Fl.)
(W.Winds)
JAKE: (Sandy calls the square dance)
Get the square dance
(Vln. Solo)
robusto
call - er! Whoop - ti - ay! Get the

square dance call - er! Whoop - ti - ay!
BEN:
133
Got a fair - haired won - der to
put me un - der, It's my wed - din'
(W.Winds)
(Vln. Solo)
EVERYBODY
141
day To - day is Ben's wed - din'
ff (Tutti)
(Hns.)
L.H.

145
Presto
day.
ff (Tutti) sempre
simile
154
ELIZABETH
My wed - din' day!
TEN.
TEN.
Ben's wed - din' day!
BAR.
BASS
Ben's wed - din' day!
Maestoso
fff
Attacca

Introduction to Scene VIII

No. 18

18
ff
1. The music stops as Ben and Eliz. appear
2.
sfz
Attacca

Drunk Scene

No. 19

25
1. The music repeats several times and stops as Ben says: "She's drunk anyway."
2.
Attacca

35
Vivace
ff
(Tutti)
40
(The curtain rises)
44
Moderato
fp
(Trmb.)
(Str.,W.Winds)
f espressivo
46
(Hn., Cello)
(A loud knocking is heard. Julio
lights a candle and opens the door.)
(Strs.)
mf

58
3
3
3
1. The music stops as Jennifer says, "Buenos Noches"
66
(Str., W.Winds, Hn.)
f
3
3
f
2.
pp
(Dialogue continues)

No. 20

Carino Mio

Cue: **JULIO:** Where can I take you, querida? Where can we go?..... Even my claim, which is not so good, brings in a few ounces every day. By the end of next year....

The music begins.

JULIO:
84
mi - o, my love is strong - er. We'll live
mf (add Hn., Trmb.)
on a hill where the an - gels play; A - way
ten.
ten.
from the world that we knew; And I'll
92
rubato
a tempo
mf
bring a rose to you ev - 'ry day. Ca - ri - no
rit.
a tempo
p

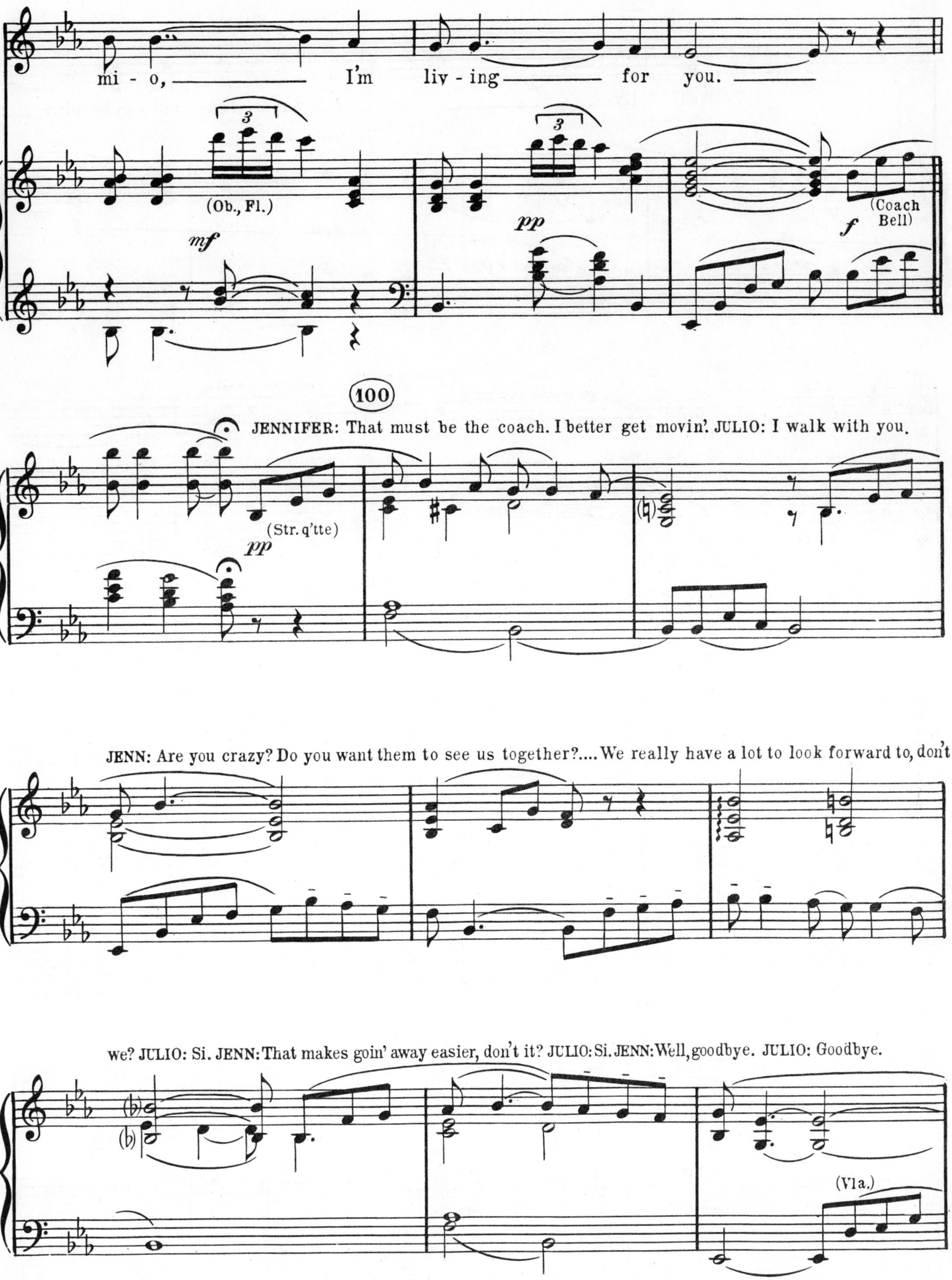

mi - o, I'm liv - ing for you.

(Ob., Fl.) *mf* *pp* *f* (Coach Bell)

100

JENNIFER: That must be the coach. I better get movin'. JULIO: I walk with you.

(Str. q'tte) *pp*

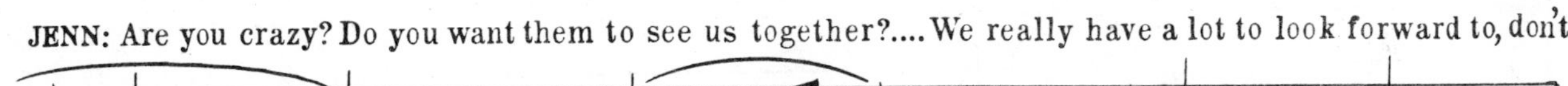

we? JULIO: Si. JENN: That makes goin' away easier, don't it? JULIO: Si. JENN: Well, goodbye. JULIO: Goodbye.

108
JULIO:
We'll live on a hill where the an - gels play,
ten.
mf (Strs.)
A - way from the world that we knew;
rubato
a tempo
116
And I'll bring a rose to you ev - 'ry day;
mf (add W. Winds)
(Hn.)
rit.
a tempo
Ca - ri - no mi - o, I'm liv - ing for you.
f allarg.
(Tutti)
ff
Attacca

There's A Coach Comin' In

No. 21

TENORS
22
MINERS: (looking in the direction of the approaching coach)
There's a coach com-in' in! If you lis-ten you can hear it a
BARITONES
BASSES
There's a coach com-in' in! If you lis-ten you can hear it a
mf
(Strs.)
30
clip-clop-pin' o-ver the hill; And the sound that you
clip-clop-pin' o-ver the hill; And the sound that you
(W. Winds obbl.)
(Trmb.)
hear Is as good to your ear As the call of a wild whip-per-
hear Is as good to your ear As the call of a wild whip-per-
(Brass)
ff

38
will. There's a coach com-in' in! You can feel it get-tin'
will. There's a coach com-in' in! You can feel it get-tin'
f
mf (Strs.)
near, All at once and it bursts in-to view
near, Bursts in-to view, And it
near, All at once and it bursts in-to view
near, Bursts in-to view, And it
(Trmb.)
46
looks to your eye Like it fell from the sky, Like a coach full o'
looks to your eye Like it fell from the sky, Like a coach full o'

54
dreams come true. For it's bring - in' me eyes that are
dreams come true. For it's bring - in' me eyes that are
(Brass)
ff
f
Hi - yah!
wine, Hi -
moon - light; And it's car - ry - in' lips that are wine,
Hi - yah!
wine, Hi -
moon - light; And it's car - ry - in' lips that are wine,
(Brass)
(Brass)
yah!
62
pil - lows
com - in' with arms that are pil - lows, Yah! And this
yah!
pil - lows, Yah!
And it's com - in' with arms that are pil - lows And this
(W. Winds)
(Brass)
ff
f

(unis)
eve - nin' it all will be mine. There's a coach com - in'
(unis)
eve - nin' it all will be mine. There's a coach com - in'
70
(Brass)
(W. Winds, Strs.)
f sempre
in! Now it's rid - in' in the clear, And the sound of it grows to a
in! Now it's rid - in' in the clear, And the sound of it grows to a
78
din. Now there ain't far to go!
din. No, there ain't far to
ff (Tpt.)
(Trmb.)

Whoa!
Whoa!
— Now they're hol - ler - in' "Whoa"! There's a
go! Yes, they're hol - ler - in' "Whoa"! There's a
(Tpt.)
(Trmb.)
(Tutti)
86
90
coach com - in' in! There's a coach com - in' and it's in!
in!
coach com - in' in! There's a coach com - in' and it's in!
in!
pp
If you lis - ten you can hear It a clip - clop - pin' o - ver the
pp
If you lis - ten you can hear
pp (Strs.)

98

hill; —— And the sound that you hear is as good to your

(Fl. obbl.)

cresc. *poco* *a* *poco*

Yah! Yah! There she is! Hoo -

ear As the call of a wild whip-per-will. —— There's a

Yah! Yah! There she is! Hoo -

ff (Brass)

f (Tutti with Banjo)

106 ray! Hoo - ray!

coach com-in' in You can feel it get-tin' near, All at

ray! Hoo - ray! You can feel it get-tin' near ——

view
once and it bursts in - to Bursts in - to view, And it
view
Bursts in - to view, And it
114
(unis)
looks to your eye Like it fell from the sky, Like a
(unis)
looks to your eye Like it fell from the sky, Like a
122
coach full o' dreams come true.
Yah! Yah!
coach full o' dreams come true.
For it's bring - in' me eyes
(W.Winds)
f sempre

Yah!
Hi - yah!
Yah!
Yah!
Yah!
that are moon - light,
And it's car - ry - in' lips that are
(Brass)
130
Hi - yah!
Com - in' with arms that are pil - lows,
pil - lows,
wine;
And it's com - in' with arms that are pil - lows,
(Brass)
Yah! And this eve - nin' it all will be mine! There's a
(unis)
And this eve - nin' it all will be mine! There's a
(Brass)
R.H.
ff (Tutti)

138
coach com - in' in! Now it's rid - in' in the clear, And the
coach com - in' in! Now it's rid - in' in the clear, And the
sound of it grows to a din; Now there
sound of it grows to a din;
(Tpt.)
marcato
146
ain't far to go Now they're hol - ler - in'
No, there ain't far to go.
accel. poco a poco
(Trmb.)
(Tpt.)
accel. poco

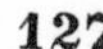

154

"Whoa!" "Whoa!" (unis.)

"Whoa!" There's a coach com - in' in, And the

Yes, they're hol - ler - in' "Whoa!" There's a coach com - in' in, And the

(Trmb.)

a poco

Presto

coach com - in' came to - day!

coach com - in' came to - day!

cresc. molto

fff

Attacca

The Fandangos' Entrance and Dance

No. 22

Lento
(Str. trem.)
(The men look on in wide-
33
Fl.
fff > pp subito
(Cl.) p
mf
scherzando
34
eyed silence as the
36
Fandangos step out
mf
(Bsn.)
p (Cls.) legato
p
(Cymb.)
(Tom-tom)
mf cantabile
(Cl.)
(Ob.)
p
one by one and
40
move among the crowd)
f corto
(Hn.)
(Trpt.) mf
(Bells)
8va
p
(The Fandangos and men
start dancing together.)
43
f
Guitar
p
(add Trpt.)
(Hn.)
molto
(add Trmb.)
(Tutti)
ff
68
con spirito

Allegro robusto
104
106
115
fff
f (Trpt.) (sempre secco)
(Hn.)
3
(Hn.)
3
(Hn.)

ff
(Trmb.)
fff
121
Più animato
123
mf (Str., W Winds)
(Str.)
131
sfz
(W.Winds)
(Trpt.)
139
sffz>f
(Hn.)

147
(Hn.)
(Trmb.)
sfz
(Tutti)
155
Allegro robusto
fff
157
f con spirito
(Hn.)
3
W.Winds
(Hn.)
3

164 W.Winds *tr* *ff*

166 *leggiero* *f*

(Trpt.)

('Cello) 3 3 3

sfz (Tutti) *fff*

173 Più animato

176

(Trmb.) *mf* (Strs.)

(Hn.)

183

(W.Winds)
f
(Trmb.,Tuba)
191
(Str.
obbl.) brillante
199
207
(W.Winds)
p grazioso
f>p
f>p
215
Hn.

ff subito
(Str., Trmb.)
223
Tempo di valse
231
(Tutti)
241
(Sax.)
f cantabile
ff
(Str., Trpt.)
(Hn.)

249
(Hn.)
(Trpt.)
255
mf cantabile
(Hn., Trmb.)
259
f
(Tutti)
espr.
267
(Trmb.
mf
(Tutti)
f poco accel.
(Trmb., Tuba)
275
Vivace
cresc.
277
(W.Winds)
ff

(add Sax.)
(Trmb.)
285
286
294
(Tutti)

(Brass)

302

(Sax.)

310

(Tutti)

6

fff

Attacca

The Fandangos' Exit

No. 23

No. 24

Finaletto

Allegro moderato

(he appears)
— I sud-den-ly see them come true.
(Str.)
pp
STEVE: Julio! You know a lot about minin'. What happens when one end of a vein goes?
rubato
(Cl.)
32
JULIO: Means pretty soon it dry up all over.
ten.
Why?
STEVE: I got a claim on the north hill. It ran out this mornin'.
JULIO: Santa Maria!
ff (Tutti)
(They look at each other for a moment meaningfully. Julio walks up and looks after where Jennifer departed)
Allegro passionato
Allargando
(Tuba Timp.)
Lento
(curtain)
sfz
fff
(End of Act I)

Entr'acte

No. 25

espress.
(Strs., W.Winds)
(add Hns.)
cresc. poco
a
poco

(add Brass)
cresc.
ff
③ Molto moderato (𝅗𝅥 = ♩)
(Cl.)
f (Strs.)
mf
espress.
(Hn.)
(Cello)
(Str.)
3
p
molto rit.
f (Str., & W.Winds)
Moderato
sempre espressivo
(Trmb. Solo)
mf

9
poco cresc.
(Str., W.Winds)
f
17
poco rit.
(Timp., Tuba)
(Cello)
Meno mosso
25
p
poco cresc.

f più ritard.
mf
Vivo
sf
f (Str., W. Winds)
ff (add Brasss)
Allegro vivace
(Tutti sempre)
9

17
sf
sf
f
(Hns.)
(Str.)
25
(Brass)
(Str.)
(Brass)
(Tutti)
W.Winds
33
mf (Hns.,Trmb.)
41
(add Trpts.)

f (Tutti)
sf
sf
49
(Trpt.)
57
ff marcato
(Trmb.)
(Trpt.)
(Trmb.)
65
(Trpt.)
(Brass)
ff brilliante
poco sostenuto
fff Attacca

Hand Me Down That Can o' Beans

No. 26

38
Out the win-der go the beans, Out the win-der go the beans,
Out the win-der go the beans, I had a luck-y day!
46
MINERS and FANDANGOS
Ma - ry! Ma-ma-ma - Ma - ry! My sweet ca-
f (add Brass)
na - ry, We're go-in' out this eve-nin'!

54
Ma - ry! Ma - ma - ma - Ma - ry! I'm gon - na
take you out to - night! So
(unis.)
62
Hand me down that can o' beans, Hand me down that can o' beans,
(Str., W. Winds)
Hand me down that can o' beans, I'm throw - in' it a - way!
sf

70
Out the win-der go the beans, Out the win-der go the beans,
Out the win-der go the beans, Go the beans, Go the beans,
Good times are here to stay!
ff
106
(Saxes)

114
sf
MINERS and FANDANGOS
122
So hand me down that can o' beans,
(add Brass)
f
Hand me down that can o' beans, Hand me down that

can o' beans, I'm throw - in' it a - way!
sf
130
Out the win-der go the beans, Out the win-der go the beans,
Out the win-der go the beans,
(Tutti)
marc.
Good times are here to stay!
ff
sfz
Attacca

No. 27

Rope Dance

23
(W.Winds)
mf
(Str., Banjo)
f robusto
37
(W.Winds)
mf scherzando
(Pete fires his revolver into the air.)
sf
cresc.
poco a poco

(Trpt.)
ff
robusto
(Str., Banjo)
51
(Str., W. Winds)
mf
f
mf
(Trpt.)
ff
robusto
(Brass)
f
63
(Banjo)
(Brass)

(Banjo)
(Strs.)
(Trpt.)
(Trmb.)
(The girls shriek as Pete cracks a whip)
77
(W.Winds)
sf
(Trmb)
(Banjo)
ff robusto
(W.Winds)
sf
(Trmb.)
(Banjo)
(W Winds)
sf
(Trmb.)
(Banjo)

110
(Banjo and Mandolin soli)
mf leggiero
1
(Pete makes advances to Yvonne)
(W.Winds)
f
(Trpt.)
mf
(W.Winds)
f
(She slaps his face)
(Trpt.)
mf
Più Lento
9
(Strs. and Oboe)
p molto espressivo

(He harnesses her with her skip-rope and they dance)
17
(add W.Winds)
p
(Hns.)
L.H.
(Trpts.)
crescendo
(The crowd shouts
f
approval and dances around them.)
25
Allegro
(Tutti)
34
ff
(Banjo)
f

(Banjo)
ff (Tutti)
f
ff
(The crowd claps in admiration of Yvonne and Pete's dancing.)
42 Allegro con spirito
(Tutti)

51
(Strs.)
f
57
(add Oboe)
f
cantabile
61
mf
65
(Trmb., Tuba)
ff

76
L'istesso tempo
(Again the crowd shows approval.)
(Tutti)
ff
84
molto con brio
93
(Banjo)
(Tutti)

101

(Banjo)

(Str.)

(W. Winds)

(Str.)

(W. Winds)

112 Poco meno *(Pete renews his advances.)*

(Trpt. soli)

f

(Oboe)

mf *cantabile*

120 *(Yvonne tries to evade him.)*

(Trpt.)

f

(Oboe)
mf
128
(He follows her)
(W.Winds)
cresc.
poco
a
(She turns to him...... and leaps into his arms)
poco
136
Allegro Maestoso
fff (Tutti)
(Timp., Tuba)
sf Dialogue

No. 28

Can-Can

Cue: BEN: Crocker, would you mind seeing Elizabeth to the cabin?
CROCKER: I'd be glad to, Ben.
BEN: Come on, Jake, where's the girl? Announce her!

JAKE: Ladies and Gentlemen! Presenting the grand, unique, demoniac can-can dancer of Paris, France, in what might well be her farewell performance! Miss Mademoiselle Suzanne Duval!

9c
(add Hns., Str.)
mf secco
cresc.
poco
a
poco
10
(Finally she selects Rocky, the most ungainly youth in
f
cre - scen -
the crowd, to dance with him her celebrated Can - Can.)
do
poco
a
poco
Tutti
ff sempre
11
Allegro con spirito

12

13
molto
fff
(W.Winds)
14
mf
8va
(Tutti)
15
molto
fff
(W.Winds)
mf
16

17
rall.
(Trpt.)
mf
f (Trmb., Tuba)
(Trpt.)
mf
poco
a
poco
f (Trmb., Tuba)
mf
f
ff sempre
riten.
(Trmb. Hn.)
20 Meno mosso
21 Allegro con spirito
accel.
(Ten. Sax.)
3

cresc.
22 L'istesso tempo
(Rocky tries to undress Suzanne, but
fff pesante
(Tutti)
(Saxes soli)
she beckons to Janney to follow her outside.)
(Brass)
(Rocky continues to dance with other girls who perform virtuoso feats)
(Tutti)
f leggiero
(Trpt.)

23
(Saxes)
(Trpt.)
(Saxes)
(Trpt.)
sempre con spirito
ff
mf
ff
mf
ff
fff
(Saxes)
24 Pesante
(Brass)
3

(Suzanne returns)
(Ten. Sax.)
(Tutti)
ff
Allegro vivace
sempre
9
(She dances with the crowd.)
(Trmb)
(Trpt.)
17

25
(Sax.)
33
(Trpts.)
41
(Strs.)

49
(Saxes)
(Trpts.)
sfz
(Tutti)
61
(Saxes)
ff sempre
69
(Trpt.)

84
(Saxes)
(Tutti)
100
(The crowd
pesante
collapses one by one.)

112
(Suzanne alone keeps dancing.)
sfz p subito
(Strs.)
120
(Ten. Sax.)
128
(Alto Sax.)
136
(Gradually the crowd returns to life and finishes the Can-Can.)
(Strs.)
pp
(Saxes)
mf

144 Strs.

pp

(Saxes)

mf

152

(Trpt.)

f

(Str., W.Winds)

cre - scen -

(Trmb.)

do poco a poco rit - en - uto

168 Allegro *(They conclude with a spectacular parade.)*

fff (Tutti)

184
ff
(Trmb.)

208
fff
(Tutti sempre)
sfz
sfz
sfz
(The dancing ends.)
221
(Tutti)
ff
dim.
poco
a
poco
mf (Str., W.Winds)

dimin.
237
CHERIE: Get up! All of you! (Dialogue continues)
(Strs)
pp
(The music fades as Julio says: "Senor Jake".....)
ppp
Dialogue

No. 29

Movin' Motive

JAKE: Well, there's always tomorrow night.
JOE: No, there ain't. *(The music begins)*

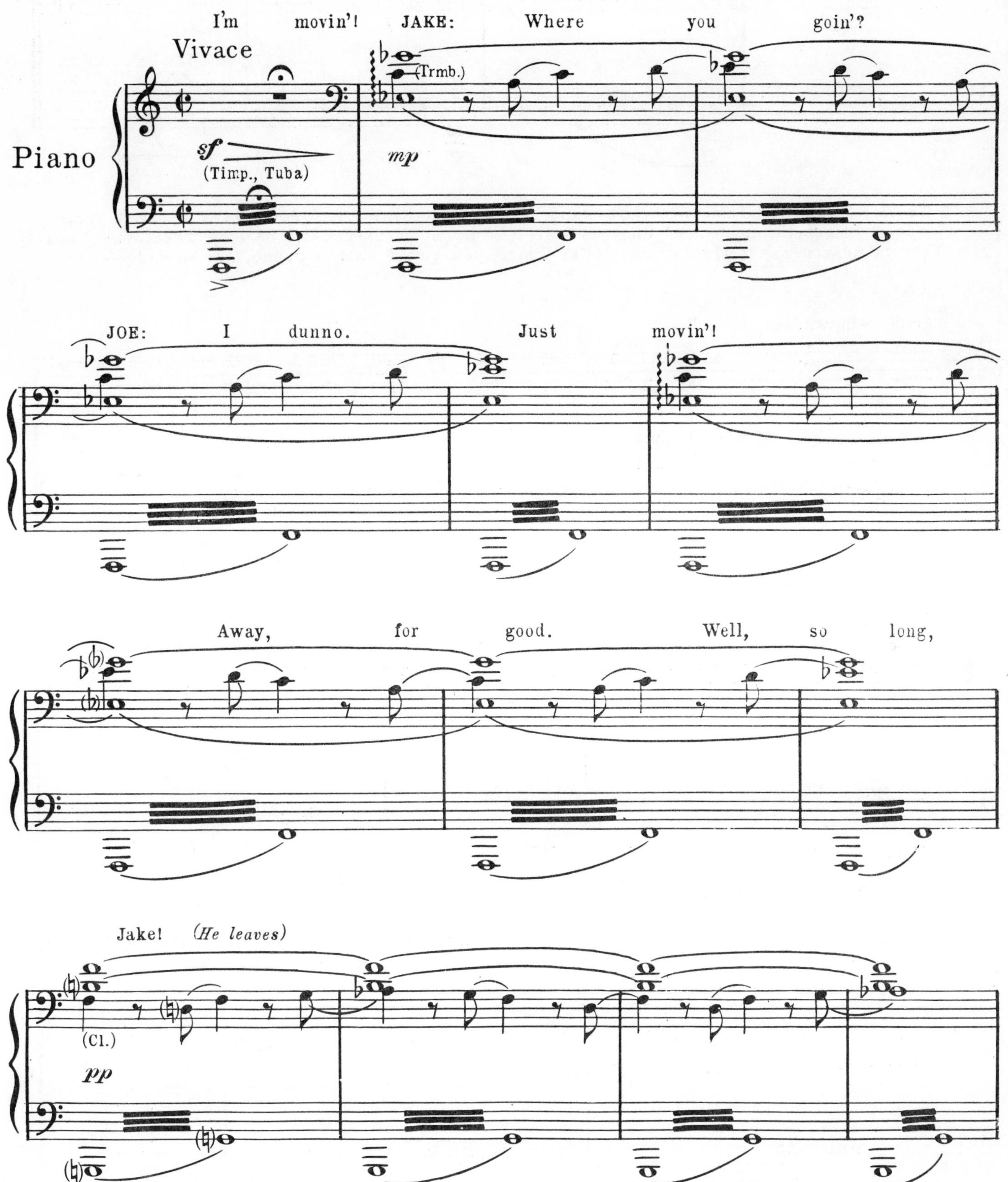

That's right, dearie. This town can't stand another 'ard winter..... Some blokes saved their money, Elizabeth, and one o' them is called Edgar P. Crocker. SAM: So long, Jake. When you get to heaven say hello for me. JAKE: Where you goin'? SAM: I dunno. *(The music begins.)*

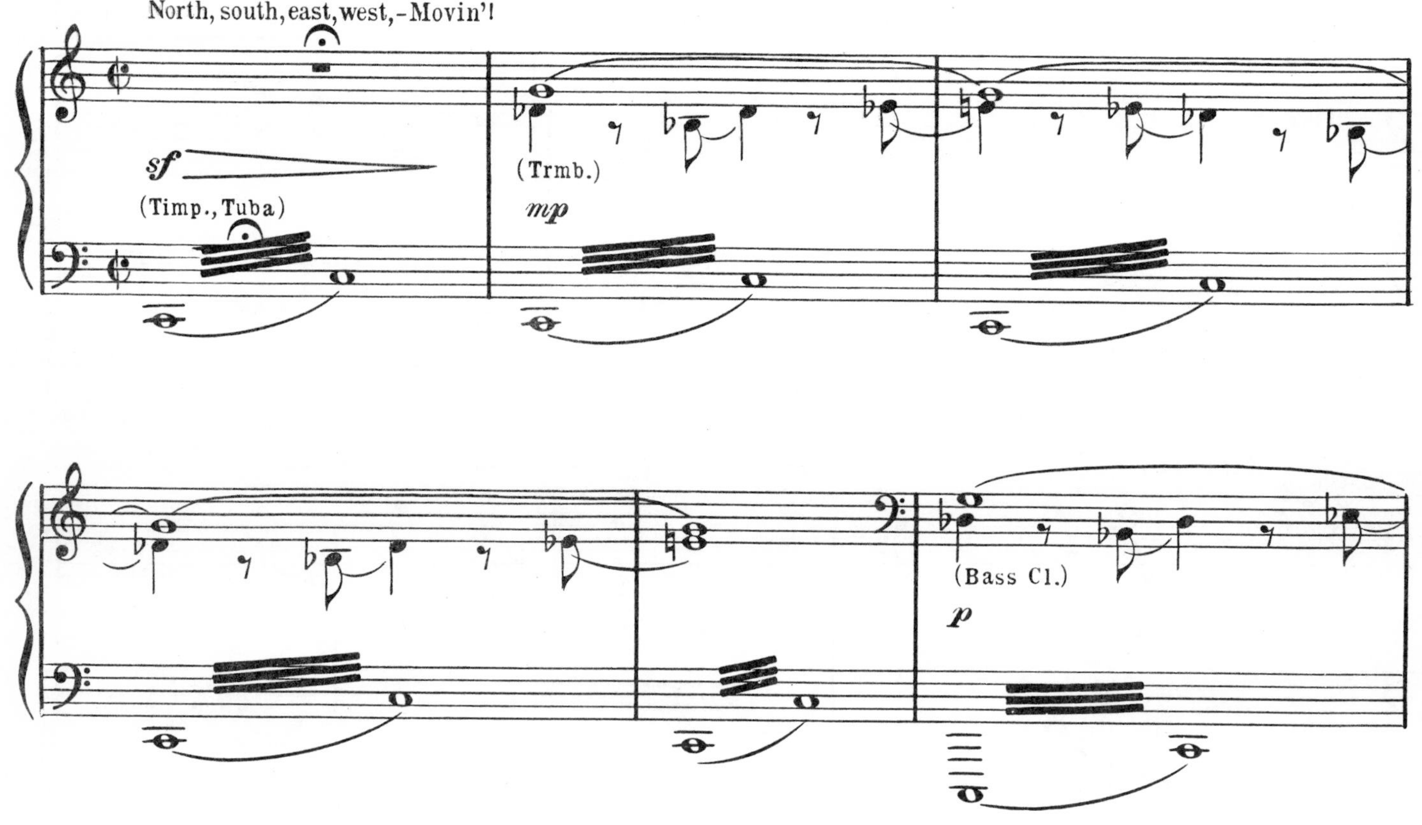

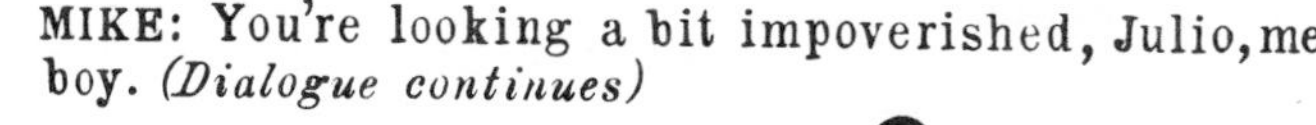
MIKE: You're looking a bit impoverished, Julio, me boy. *(Dialogue continues)*

Another Autumn

No. 30

Cue: JULIO: You're crazy, senor.... you either freeze or go mad.
MIKE: Or you stay here and starve. I tell you, lad, we could be up and back before the snow ever falls.
(The music begins)

SANDY: What are you gonna do now? STEVE: I dunno. I wrote my wife and asked her if I could
(Cl.)
23
come home even though I'm busted. She wrote me to stay out here and keep tryin'. That's how she is,
(Fl.)
pp
a born fighter. Are you gonna go back home? SANDY: I reckon if I can't find no place else to go, I'll have to.
(Cl.)
3
poco rit.
31
JULIO:
Why have all the dreams Been bro-ken wide a - part? And
p (Str.)
a tempo
where is all the hope that was in my heart?
(Cl.)

39

STEVE: Sandy, if you'd held on to your gold, what was you gonna do with it? SANDY: I was just thinkin'

pp

(Hn.)

47

about that. I had somethin' in mind, but I just can't remember what it was. PETE: You gotta have land, Yvonne.

(Cl.)

That's the only thing that counts. Some day I'll dig enough and I'll come and get you. You'll see. You'll see.

poco rit.

54 Tempo I

JULIO:

An - oth - er au - tumn, I've known the chill be - fore;

p (Str., W. Winds)

— But ev-'ry au - tumn, — I feel it more and more. —
62
— For you can dream in Spring, — When ev-'ry hope is high; —
— But when the Fall comes in They all be-gin to
70
fade and die. — An-oth-er au - tumn, — So sweet when all is well; —

— But how it haunts you, When all is wrong.
cre - scen - do
f (Tutti)
78
— For one thing time has shown, If you're a-lone when au - tumn comes,
p (Str., W.Winds)
— You'll be a - lone All win-ter long.
(Hn.)
calmando
rit.
(Pete and Yvonne dance quietly, expressing the meaning of Julio's song)
86
Poco animato
(Oboe)
mf

94
(Bssn.)
(Vlns.)
102
(Viola)
dim.
(Cello)
pp
p espr.
106
Andante molto espressivo
(Str., Hns.)

114
(Vlns.)
mf espr.
(Hns., Cl.)
(Vlns.)
122
f cantabile
(Bs. Cl.)

126
dim.
poco
a
poco
p
130
rall.
136 Lento
ff (Tutti)

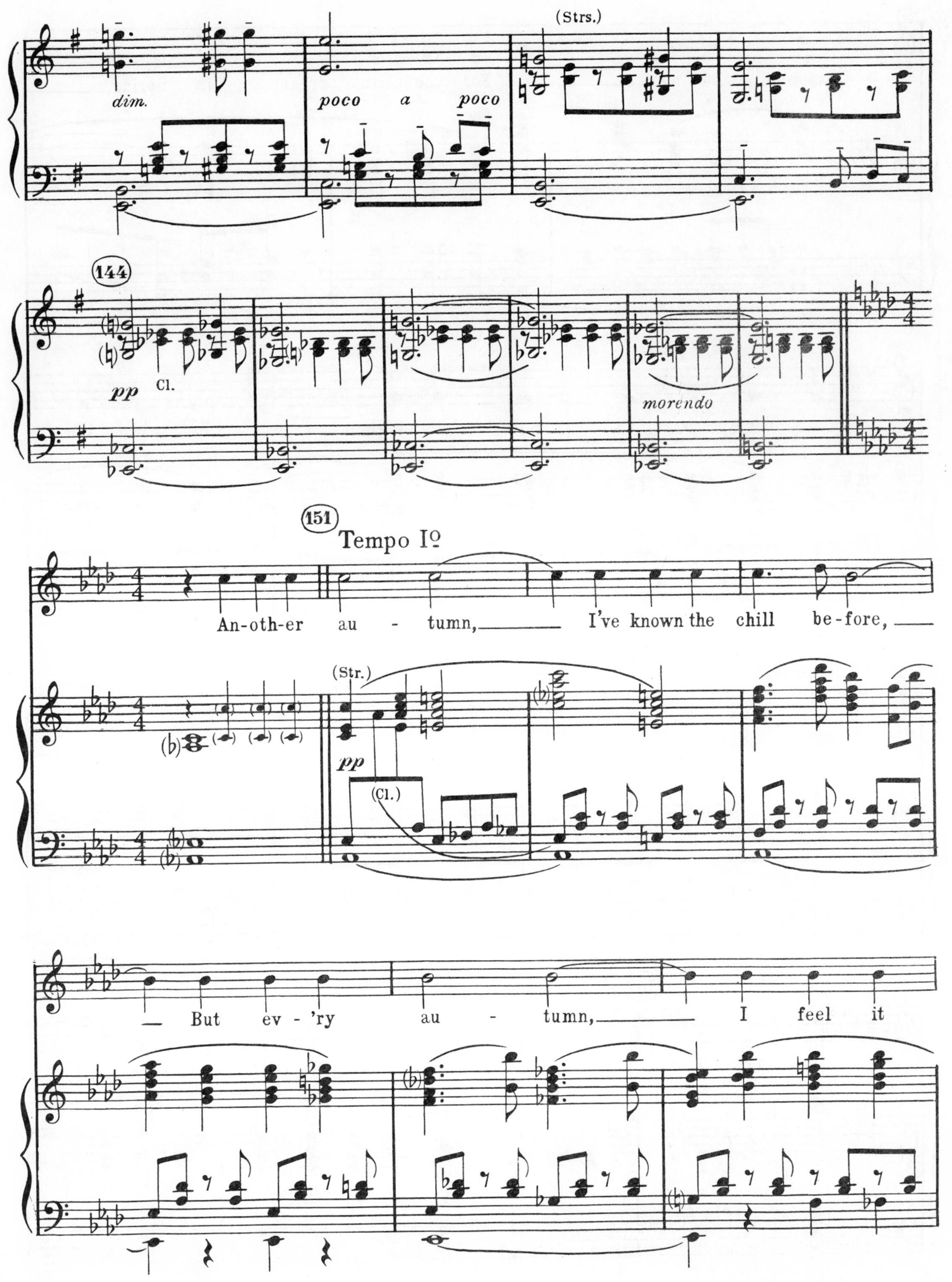
(Strs.)
dim.
poco a poco
144
pp
Cl.
morendo
151
Tempo I°
An-oth-er au - tumn, I've known the chill be-fore,
(Str.)
pp
(Cl.)
But ev - 'ry au - tumn, I feel it

159
more and more. For you can dream in Spring,
When ev - 'ry hope is high; But when the
fall comes in, They all be-gin to fade and die.
167
An - oth - er au - tumn, So sweet when all is well;
p
3
3

— But how it haunts you When all is wrong.
cresc.
f (Tutti)
175
— For one thing time has shown, If you're a-lone when
p (Str., W. Winds)
au - tumn comes, You'll be a - lone All win-ter
(Hn.)
calmando
long.
(Tutti)
f
sffz
Dialogue

No. 31

Introduction to "Movin'"

Cue: JULIO: You think we can get back by winter?
MIKE: If we leave right away.
JULIO: I go with you, señor.
STEVE: Where you goin', Mike? *(The music begins)*

No. 32

Movin'

Vivace
(Trpts.)
(The curtain rises)
Piano
ff
3
SANDY:
ED: (Packing his equipment)
How's it, Ed? I'm mov - in'. Had an - oth - er aw - ful week.
(Strs., W.Winds)
mf sempre
Not a speck o' yel - ler float - in' up or down the creek.
11
SANDY:
ED:
SANDY:
Where you bound? Ain't cer - tain. Have you thought o' Hang-man's Bar?

ED:
Hear they're do - in' lous - y, And be - sides, it's aw - ful far, But I'm
19
mo - vin'! Mo - vin'! Mo - vin'! Mo - vin'!
(Hns.)
sf
23
ED: BILL:
How's it, Bill? I'm bust - ed. Had an - oth - er noth - in' day.
(Cl.)
mf
sf
ED: BILL:
What 'dja bring in? Ze - ro. Not e - nough to e - ven weigh.
mf
sf

(31)

BILL: How's it, Jack? JACK: It's rot-ten! Half an ounce is all I've got-ten. Think I'll

mf sf

hit the grit and wan-der To So-no-ry town up yon-der. SANDY: I don't

mf sf

(39)

know a-bout So-no-ra. ED: Yeah, they're weep-in' in So-no-ra. JASPER: Hey! A

mf f

(43)

guy who just come from Dead Gulch ______ Says they're

strik - in' veins this size! Says that

51

ev - 'ry day some - one's find - in'

(Vlns.)

(b)

ED: Let's go to Dead Gulch!

Nug - gets big as el - e - phants' eyes.

(Cl.)

sf

p

(Trmb.)

(Cl.)

59

JASPER:

May - be he was ly - in', He was aw - ful full o' rum.

(Strs.)

mf

sf

(Cl.)

For a guy who struck it, He was sure a wear-y bum.
mf
sf
67
SAM:
JOHANSEN:
What-cha think, Jo-han-sen? T'ink I look for bet-ter ground.
mf
sf
ED:
SAM:
JOHANSEN:
Where you gon-na find it? Where you go-in? Where you bound? First I
mf
mf
75
t'ink I go to Luck-y Ci-ty; Den I
(sempre staccato)
cre - scen - do poco a poco
(Bass Cl., Banjo)

hear is wild and wool - y town. Den I
(Cl.)
cresc.
f
83
t'ink I go to Don - key Val - ley; Den dey
mf
tell me some-one burn it down.
(Cl.)
sf
91
JASPER:
Much - ee, where you go - in'? Have you picked your-self a camp?
mf
sf

*Cantonese dialect, transcribed into approximate English phonetics. (English translation: "God bless us, everything will be all right.")

What will I get? I ain't e-quipped to say, But
What will I get? I ain't e-quipped to say, But
139
Who gives a damn, We're on our
Who gives a damn, We're on our
f sempre
(Tutti)
way!
way!
ff
sffz
Curtain
Attacca

Introduction to Scene III

No. 33

All For Him*

No. 34

ELIZABETH: He's going to be amazed at how you've grown up.
JENNIFER: Do you really think so? *(The music begins)*

***NOTE:** *In the New York production, this number was also sung in the keys of C and D.*

JENN:
Tempo di Valse
I have know - ledge to spare in my head
(Strs., W. Winds)
p sempre
And there're so man - y books I have read,
9
But what - ev - er I've learned, Far as I am con -
cerned, I was stor - ing up all for him.
(W. Winds)

17

— Al - ex - an - der, they tell me, was great; ——

— Mo - zart wrote a so - na - ta at eight. ——

25

— When he feels like a chat, We can talk a - bout

that; 'Cause I stud - ied it all —— for him. ——

(W. Winds)

33
All for him! All for him!
mf
f
brillante
(Tutti)
mf
f
Will the sun and the moon nev - er dim.
mp
41
All for him! All for him! All for
mf
Poco calmo
him, all for him, all for him! I can
p
(Str.)
f (Tutti)
p

43
say, "Thank you, no." In a
Hns.
way that comes out, "Thank you, yes." I can
57
knit. I can sew. I can
dine like a queen with-out drop-ping a bean. And if

49a
we are in France, I know
p
how to say, "Ou est la plume?" I can
57a
write. I can dance. I can
curt - sy but not Make an In - di - an squat. One and
pp

65
Tempo di Valse
one al - ways add up to two. I don't
(Str., W.Winds)
p sempre
know why they do, but they do. But it's
73
all right with me, And I won't dis - a - gree 'Cause I
fig - ure it's all for him. Ne - ro
(W.Winds)

81
fid - dled while Rome was a - fire. If he
did - nt, then some - one's a liar. It's im -
port - ant, I guess, But it is - n't un - less, He was
do - ing it all for him. All for
(W. Winds)
mf

97
him! All for him! There's a
f brillante
(Tutti)
mf
f
mp
sum - mer and win - ter and fall; All for
mf
him! All for him! Ev - 'ry -
f
thing I ev - er knew, And all I ev - er do, is all for him!
(Str., Bs. Cl)
mp
ff (Tutti)
sf Dialogue

No. 35

Wand'rin' Star*

JENNIFER: And... Julio?

BEN: You mean that Mexican feller who used to change his shirt every week? No, he's gone.... You're a lady now, Jen. Just about the ladyest lady I ever saw. You don't belong in the gold country.

JENNIFER: What... what about you, Pa? I thought this was your home. *(The music begins)*

BEN: Me? I'm movin', too. I'll go on to another town and try again. Some folks ain't never meant to have a home. I guess I'm one of 'em.

NOTE: In the New York production, this number was also sung in the keys of Ab and B.

1876

I was born under a
wan - d'rin' star.
11
Stay - in' put can kill ya; Stand - in' still's a curse; To
(Hn.)
set - tle down can drive ya mad, But mov - in' on is worse.

I was born under a
wan - d'rin' star.
19
When I learned to talk the word they taught me was "Good-bye";
p (Hn.)
That, and "Where's my hat?" are all I'll need until I die.

Ach - in' for to stop and al - ways ach - in' for to go;
Search - in', but for what I nev - er will know.
27
I was born Un - der a
p
wan - d'rin' star.
(Cl.)
poco espr.

I was born Un-der a wan - d'rin' star.
Drink - in' makes ya wan-der;
Wan - d'rin' makes ya gray;
So pour me out a couple o' shots And
I'll be on my way.
I was
(Hn.)
39

born under a wan - d'rin'
star, A wan - d'rin', wan - d'rin',
(Bs. Cl.)
star.
(Cl.)
47
When I get to Heav - en, Tie me to a tree; Or
p
(Hn.)

I'll be-gin to roam, and soon You know where I will be.
I was born under a
wan - d'rin' star, - A wan - d'rin',
(Bs.Cl.)
wan - d'rin' star.
(Br.)
f
sfz
Curtain
Attacca

Introduction to Scene IV

No. 36

No. 37

Incidental Music

CHERRY: Julio . . . Julio . . . Think, girls. Think with your head! Julio . . . It's very hard to remember, you know. After a while there were three or four hundred Mexicans living here.
(The music begins)

Mooney. CHERRY: They went north to the hills to look for a gold lake.
Crazy fools! JENNIFER: A gold lake! Sometimes don't you get sick of
men and their dreams? CHERRY: What can you do? You can't hold a
man by holding him back. When you grow up you get used to it.
Segue

"I Talk To The Trees" Reprise

No. 38

time To stop and hear what I say;
I talk to them all in
3
3
vain. But sud - den - ly my words
(Fls.)
3
p (W.Winds)
Reach some - one el - se's ear; Touch some - one

el - se's heart strings, too. I tell you my
(Cl.)
dreams And while you're list - 'ning....
(Vls.)
(It would seem that she is about to cry.)
JENN: Thank you. (She leaves. The girls look
after her sympathetically.)
pp (Celesta)
JAKE: (with a wagon) Come on, girls. Load up. Come on! I haven't got all night. (In the general hub-bub, the curtain falls.)
(Segue)

Introduction to Scene V

No. 39

Fandango's Farewell

No. 40

BEN: Me? You go after her. She's your wife. You got the bill o' sale. Read it. I got nothin' to do with it.
STEVE: You better get movin', or you're gonna have the shortest marriage on record. *(The music begins.)*

1876

your drinks? Let's have one last one for goodbye. JAKE: You leavin' too, Ben? BEN: Well, it
looks that way. Salem, where's your next cheatin' spot gonna be? SALEM: I'm retirin', Ben.
15
The last coach is comin' through here tomorrow. I'm gettin' on it and goin' back East.
Hn.
p
(Cl.)
BEN: You are? Listen, Salem, my kid'll be on that coach too. Take care of her
pp
(Guitar and Strs.)
for me, and I'll never forget you. SALEM: Why certainly, Ben. (They clink their glasses together.)
22
(repeat if necessary)
Segue

"Rumson Town" Reprise

No. 41

(There is a moment of silence. Everybody seems hopelessly dejected. Suddenly the cries of "Strike! Strike! are heard from the street.)

No. 42 The Strike

STEVE: What the hell...?
JACK: Gold! Gold!
STEVE: They struck gold! *(The music begins)*

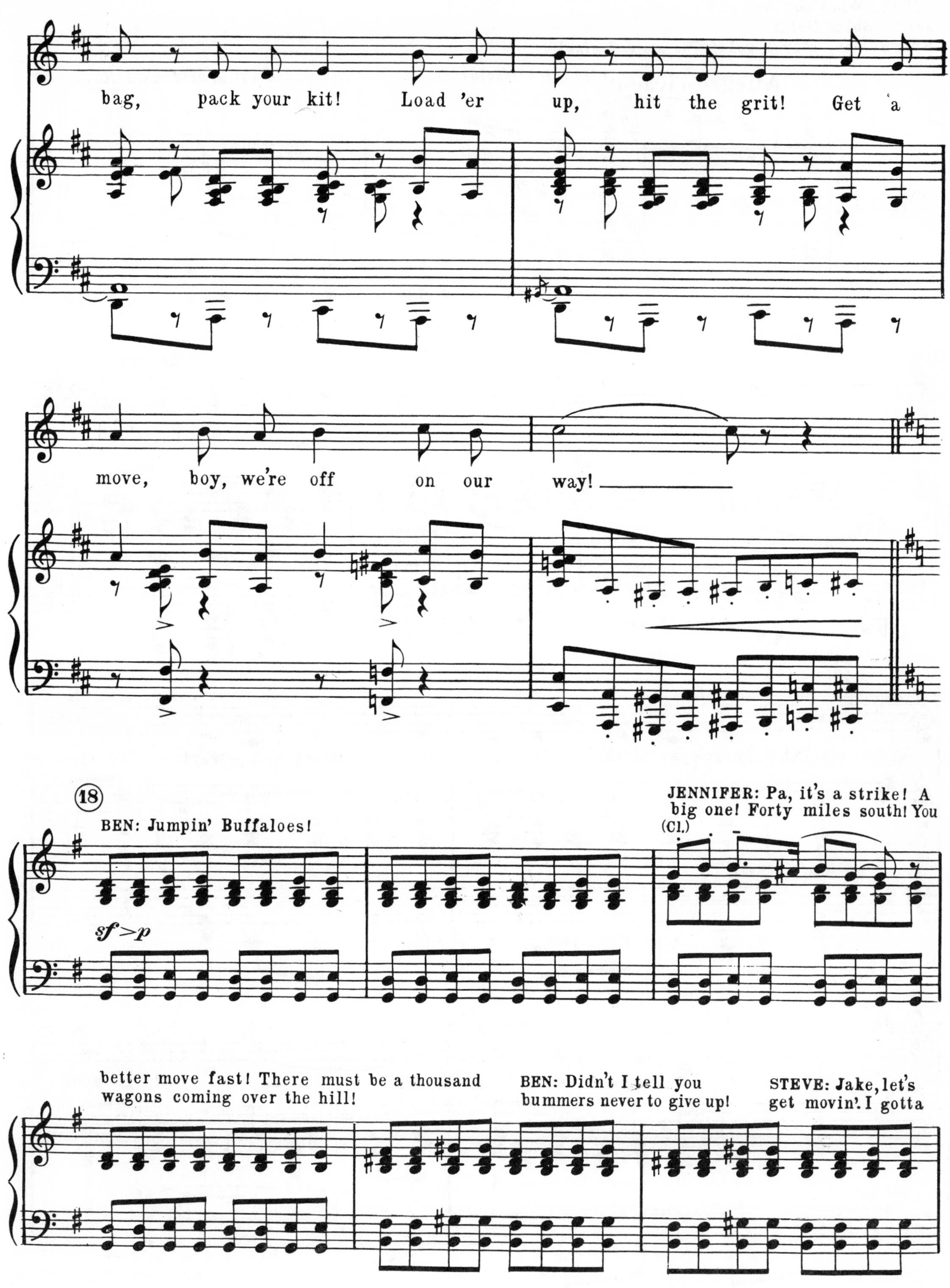

bag, pack your kit! Load 'er up, hit the grit! Get a
move, boy, we're off on our way!
18
BEN: Jumpin' Buffaloes!
sf>p
JENNIFER: Pa, it's a strike! A big one! Forty miles south! You
(Cl.)
better move fast! There must be a thousand wagons coming over the hill!
BEN: Didn't I tell you bummers never to give up!
STEVE: Jake, let's get movin'. I gotta

hit it and get home to my wife. JAKE: Cherry! It's a strike! A strike!
(Cl.)
26
29
STEVE:
Pack your bag and pack your kit, And ro-sin up your bow!
(W. Winds)
mf (Str., Mandolin)
sempre vivace
Ain't sure where we're go - in', But, be - jay-pers, here we go!
33
BEN: I'll write you as soon as I get wherever the hell I'm goin'. (He embraces her and leaves.)
(Trpt.)
(Fl.)
(Vl.)
sf>p

39
JAKE: There's a strike, honey! You go on to Denver, and round up some new girls. As soon as I hit it, I'll send
p sempre
for you. It won't be long.
43
CHERRY: No, no, Jakie! I won't wait for you. This time I come with you.
scherzando
JAKE: Sure, and we'll open up again
W.Winds and Mandolin
bigger and better than ever, and this time we'll be smarter! JENN: Goodbye, Pa! Good luck! SALEM:
JAKE:
There's a
Goodbye, Ben! I'll take care of Jennifer! Good luck, Ben!
(Ben leaves.)
mf

52
strike! There's a strike! On - ly for - ty miles a - way! Get your
Str. and Brass
sempre vivace
pan, get your pick, get your pail! Fare thee
well, fare thee well! See you all down in Hell! There's a
(He and Cherry leave)
rain - bow up the trail!

60
SALEM: It looks like the entire West is coming over the hill. Can I help
(Cl.)
sf>p
you pack, Jennifer? JENN: No, you can't, Salem. I'm not going with you. SALEM:
(Bssn.)
65
What? JENN: I'm not going with you, Salem. I'm staying here. I'm waiting for
someone. SALEM: But, Jennifer, this is going to be a difficult winter... JENN: Please, Salem. Go.
(Viola)
(Ob., Bs. Cl.)
(Salem leaves. Jennifer stands alone for a moment.)
(Str.)
molto
(Str., Trpt.)
f senza allarg.

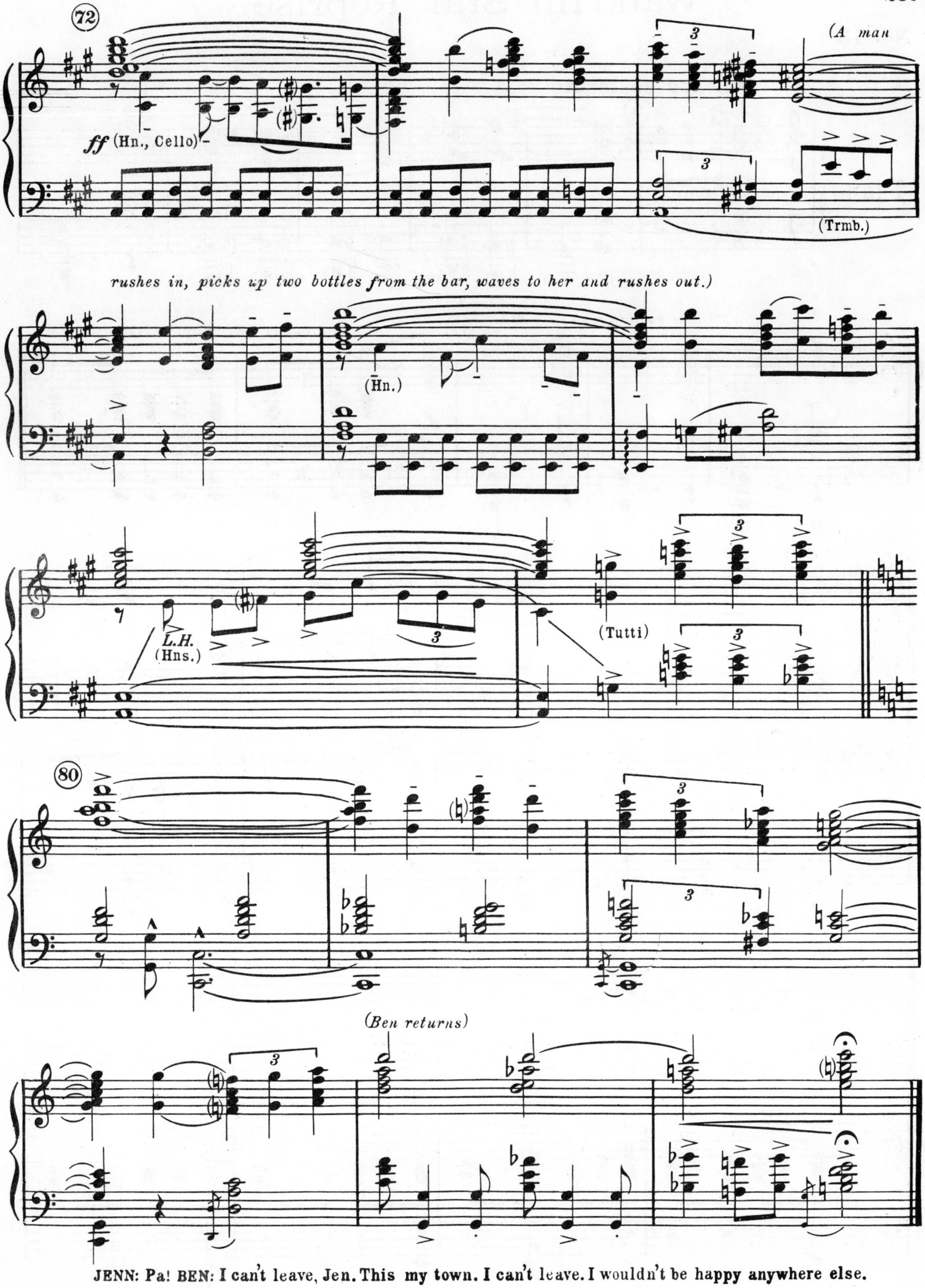

(72)

ff (Hn., Cello)

(A man

(Trmb.)

rushes in, picks up two bottles from the bar, waves to her and rushes out.)

(Hn.)

L.H. (Hns.)

(Tutti)

(80)

(Ben returns)

JENN: Pa! BEN: I can't leave, Jen. This my town. I can't leave. I wouldn't be happy anywhere else.

"Wand'rin' Star" Reprise

No. 43

29
I was born Under a
I was born Under a
wan - d'rin' star.
wan - d'rin' star.
(Trpt.)
37
STEVE:
Go-in' home to Geor-gia, Back to set-tle down; But
(Str., Hn)
p
first I'll try my luck a-gain in a new bo-nan-za town.

45
TENOR I
TENOR II
I was born Un-der a
BARITONE
BASS
I was born Un-der a
(Str., Cl.)
mf
wan - d'rin' star.
wan - d'rin' star.
53
What they taught,
f>p
What they taught me was "Good -
When I learned to talk the word they taught me was "Good -
Str. and W.W.
poco piu f

That
I'll
f>p
f>p
bye;"
That
I'll
bye;"
That and "Where's my hat?" are all I'll
(Trpts.)
sfz
need
61
Ach -
f>p
f>p
need un - til I die.
Ach -
need un - til I die.
Ach - in' for to
(Trpts.)
sfz
in'
for
what
f>p
f>p
in'
for
what
stop and al - ways ach - in' for to go;
(Trpts.)
sfz

I'll never know.
I'll never know.
Searchin', but for what I never will know.
(Brass)
69
I was born Under a
I was born Under a
(Str. and Cl.)
wan - d'rin' star,
wan - d'rin' star,

77
I was born Under a
I was born Under a
wan - - d'rin' star.
wan - - d'rin' star.
(Trpt.)
85
JAKE:
Gon-na build a pal-ace, Build it for the men; And
(Str. and Hn.)
mf
if I lose it all I'll go some-where else and try a - gain.

93
I was born
(Str. and Cl.)
Under a wan - - - d'rin' star,
TEN. I
JAKE: MINERS:
101
TEN. II
A wan - d'rin', wan - d'rin'
BAR.
BASS.
A wan - d'rin', wan - d'rin'
f (Tutti)
star.
star.
sfz (Cymb.)

109
What they taught
f>p
What they taught me was "Good -
When I learned to talk the word they taught me was "Good -
(Str. and W. Winds)
f sempre
That I'll
bye;" That I'll
bye;" That and "Where's my hat?" are all I'll
need
117
Ach
need un - til I die. Ach
need un - til I die. Ach - in' for to

in'
f>p
for
What
in'
for
What
stop and al - ways ach - in' for to go;
I'll nev - er know.
I'll nev - er know.
Search - in', but for what I nev - er will know.
125
I was born Un - der a
I was born Un - der a

157

wan — d'rin' star, — A wan -

wan — d'rin' star, — A wan -

cres - cen - do

ff (Tutti)

d'rin', wan - d'rin' star. —

d'rin', wan - d'rin' star. —

senza rit.

sffz

Curtain

Attacca

Introduction to Scene VII

No. 44

Town; — Spring is bloom - ing once a - gain in Rum - son Town. —

Well, here they are, Ben, The first crop of spring vegetables.
(The dialogue continues.)

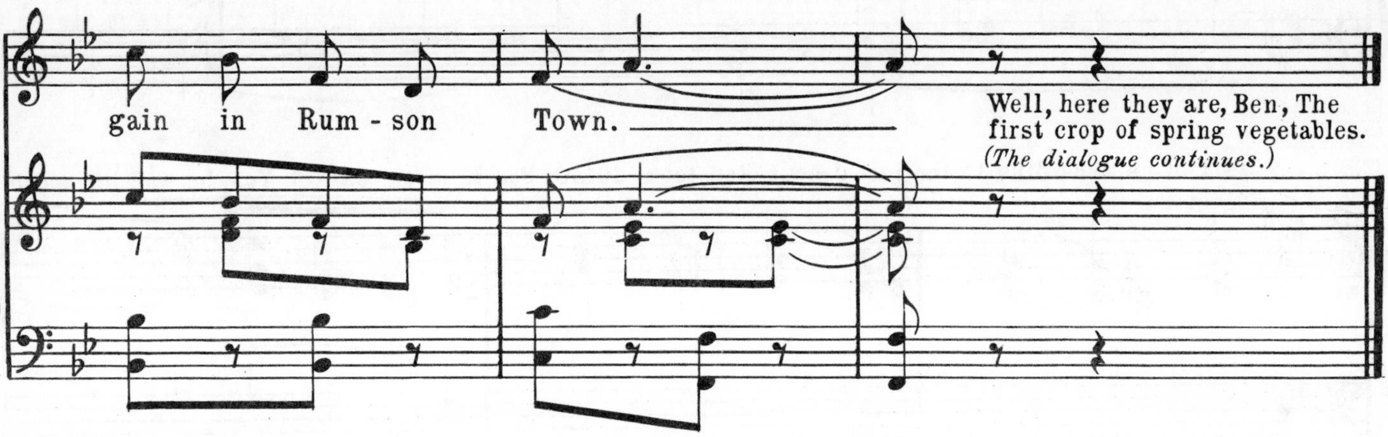

No. 45

Incidental Music

BEN: Well, when you ain't got nothin', you gotta have plans. Jennifer's in the store. She'll take care of the vegetables; I gotta mix some paint. You gotta keep plannin'. *(Ben enters the saloon. The music begins.)*

1876

would be no one here. JACOB: Oh, no. This isn't a ghost town yet. There are still a few of us left.

JULIO: Really? How many? JACOB: There's the sign. JULIO: I can't read. JACOB: I'm sorry. There are

six of us according to the last census Ben took. JULIO: Ben Rumson? JACOB: Yes, he and his daugh-

ter are still around. JULIO: What's she like now, senor? I met her once...when I stubbed my toe. JACOB: She

grew up into quite a fine lady. She's in the store if you want to see her.

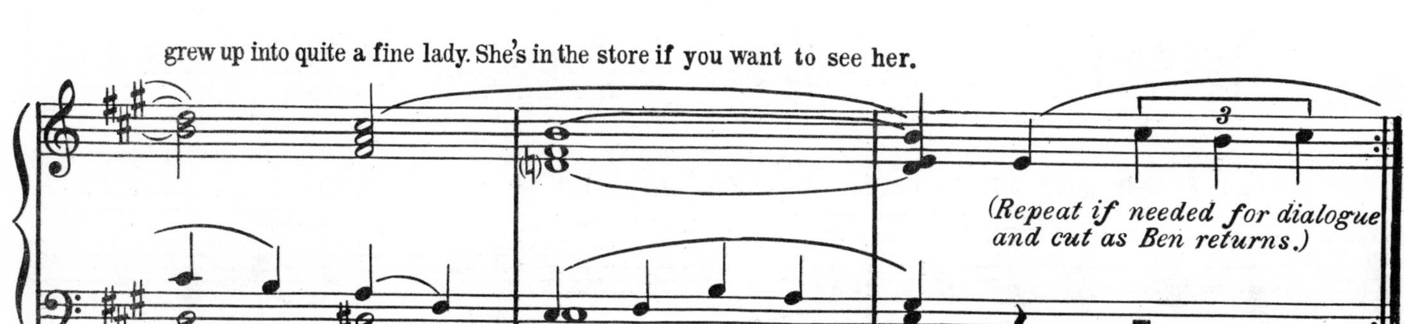

BEN: Where the hell have you been? *(Dialogue continues.)*

No. 46

Finale Ultimo

JULIO: How did she know I come back?

BEN: She didn't. But she says everybody's got to dream about something whether they get it or don't.... But you're on your way to Mexico and I got work to do, so there's no sense talkin' to you about it.

(Jennifer appears. She stops dead in her tracks when she sees Julio. The music begins.)

wa - gon And come a - long!
wa - gon And come a - long!
Where am I go-in'? I don't know. When will I be there? I ain't cer-tain.
Where am I go-in'? I don't know. When will I be there? I ain't cer-tain.
f (Tutti)
What will I get? I ain't e-quipped to say. But
What will I get? I ain't e-quipped to say. But

(Julio and Jennifer embrace.)
who gives a damn, We're on our
who gives a damn, We're on our
ff
way!
way!
cresc.
poco
a
poco
(The curtain slowly falls.)
fff
sff

End of Act II

Exit Music

No. 47

ff
L.H.
f
Andante con moto
(Str., W. Winds, Hn.)
espressivo

f
sempre

(Strings)
poco rit
mf
Allegro
f sempre
(Tutti)
sfz
W. Winds

f sempre
Tutti
accel. e cresc. poco a poco

Vivace

(Tutti)
(♩ = 𝅗𝅥)
ff sempre
sffz
Fine